BOOKS BY LORUS AND MARGERY MILNE

Water and Life 1964

Because of a Tree 1963

The Valley: Meadow, Grove and Stream 1963

The Senses of Animals and Men 1962

The Mountains 1962
LIFE *Nature Library*

The Lower Animals:
Living Invertebrates of the World 1960
with Ralph and Mildred Buchsbaum

Animal Life 1959

Plant Life 1959

Paths Across the Earth 1958

The World of Night 1956

The Mating Instinct 1954

The Biotic World and Man 1952, 1958, 1964,

Famous Naturalists 1952

A Multitude of Living Things 1947

WATER AND LIFE

LORUS & MARGERY MILNE

WATER AND LIFE

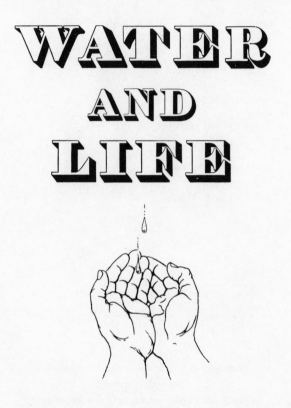

DRAWINGS BY KENNETH GOSNER

ATHENEUM : NEW YORK

1972

To Lillian *and* Rowland McElvare
whose Windridge *is a reliable oasis*
between North and South

We treasure the solid signs of civilization in cities, and tend to overlook the flowing water without which we cannot enjoy the rest. Yet in the spring of 1964, the post offices in New York City cancelled mail with these words:

CONTENTS

WATER
AND
LIFE

PROLOGUE

WHEN we think of the world we share with other people and the wild creatures, we often wonder how so many interpretations can be drawn from the same scene. A pond in the middle of a field of daisies means one thing to an artist, another to a poet, or a farmer, or a businessman, or a naturalist, or a duck, or a honeybee. Any piece of land with water has this wealth of appeals.

We have a friend who is a poet. His agile mind probes swiftly as a butterfly's tongue into the hidden meaning of a water lily, and carries away something that is simplified, distilled into an essence. As though on wings, the something flits about among the secret patterns of his inner self until it settles on one that matches well enough to ignite a conscious thought.

We have a friend who is an artist. Her union week is a world of textile patterns, of threads in the two dimensions of warp and woof, of harmonies in contrasting colors, kaleidoscopic, somber, gay. On weekends, she looks for patterns near the sea, and finds them or conjures them to suit her mood. With pigments from her palette she communicates her view in a message that is just as real—and as far from the objective evidence of the photographer's lens—as Longfellow's deft picture of a storm: "The hooded clouds, like friars,/Tell their beads in drops of rain."

3

We have a friend who is a honeybee. We meet her daily while she shops for sweets beside a pond. Sometimes she creeps cautiously to the edge of the water and stands on the wet sand while slaking her thirst. Or she rests four-footed on a leaf while using her front legs to brush from her bulging eyes the fine dust of pollen she will carry home as ingredients for bee bread. With her eyes and brain she estimates the perimeter of each blossom, and ignores those that have dropped a petal; they cease to match her secret picture of what a flower should be when sugar water awaits her in its depths.

We look at the same world and try to match its pattern with something simple enough to comprehend. Our own heritage and training convince us that we cannot ask a scientist for a final answer. A scientist merely has more facts among which to seek a pattern, and needs the same genius as the poet to pick out the bits and pieces that have true meaning. We cannot rely upon our neighbors, for each of them is a custodian of a different pattern and among them is little agreement.

Thoreau's neighbors did not understand him when he sat by the river in floodtime and noted that "the water on the meadows is quite high on account of the melting snow and rain. It makes a lively prospect when the wind blows. . . . Where the cranberry and andromeda and swamp oak and maple grow, here is a mimic sea with its gulls. At the bottom of the sea— cranberries." No farmer could view so dispassionately his inundated fields.

Much of Thoreau's short life overlapped the mature years of a German genius who viewed the world from unusual angles, and who sought to see it in the

round without traveling far from home. Johann
Wolfgang von Goethe—dramatist, poet, philosopher,
mystic, man of science—combined in one person so
many personalities that he bridges the past and the
future as well as his own time. Each of our human
friends seems to know Goethe for some one side, and
to forget the other facets in his busy life. We too show
a preference for just a few of Thoreau's many talents
—those most evident in his thoughts at Walden.

The poet and the scientist combined in Goethe
when he penned in sonorous German:

> Alles ist aus dem Wasser entsprungen,
> Alles wird durch das Wasser erhalten.

> Everything originated in the water,
> Everything will be sustained by water.

Today we can read into Goethe's words a new world
of meaning, and see that he focused on an essence of
life which grows more precious every day. All over
the world, as the numbers of people grow, so does the
need for water to sustain us. Increasingly we have
reason to treasure it and to translate Goethe's lines
into modern action.

In 1963, the Supreme Court of the United States
ruled on the apportionment of water in the Colorado
River. Almost simultaneously, the town council of
Brits, on the Crocodile River in the South African
Transvaal, adopted the motto "Life from Water."
Both are expressions of new concern over the one
resource we share with all kinds of life, and which no
life can do without. With every human birth we gain
a new reason to think of water, to explore what is
known and dreamed, and to cherish a heritage we
can enjoy into all the tomorrows.

1

OUR PORTABLE OCEAN

THE first water to condense as liquid upon the planet Earth rained down and sizzled on the cooling primeval rocks some four and a half billion years ago. Four and a half billion is about the number of heartbeats of a person who lives to be a hundred. If every beat of the centenarian's heart represents a year in the geologist's timetable, then only the last half hour of that long lifetime encompasses the whole scientific age. This is the time in which water has held a special place in man's understanding of his world.

When the great Hippocrates, "Father of Medicine," was born on the Greek island of Cos around 460 B.C., the learned men of his day had already convinced themselves from earnest contemplation that everything they saw was composed of four elements: water, earth, air, and fire. In the proportions of these four, a stone differed from a man. Into the lifetime of Chaucer and Columbus this view sufficed. Indeed, the spiral course of human understanding took nearly twenty-three centuries to make a full turn. Then the chemists accurately assayed the water of crystallization in a stone, and a biologist learned from objective evidence that every man alive is about 70 percent

water. Of every living thing, water is the most dy-
namic and essential constituent.

Today we can feel no surprise that the first artic-
ulate person to observe living things closely should
have sought for tangible materials as the components
of life. Perhaps it is significant that, in seeking equivalents for the four mystic elements, Aristotle chose
liquids: phlegm for water, black bile (*melancholia*) for
earth, blood (*sanguis*) for fire, and yellow bile (*cholia*)
for air. So ingrained did his explanation become in
Western minds that we may still speak of a person as
phlegmatic, melancholy, sanguine, or choleric. To
Aristotle, an excess of one of the four humors in a
man's "temperament" or a lady's "complexion"
produced the habitual mood. Phlegm and bile and
blood are all mostly water, with blood the most
plentiful.

Of all the fluid in a person, blood alone flows
readily from any wound. In the modern world, we
can answer Lady Macbeth's question: ". . . who
would have thought the old man to have had so much
blood in him?" A full-grown human body contains
about five quarts—ten pounds—of blood. Yet almost
half of blood is the suspended cells that confer its
bright red color. Less than three quarts are liquid
plasma, sweeping the red cells along their countless
routes from the heart and back again.

Most of the water in the body is not in the blood
stream but outside it—inside cells, and between the
cells and organs as thin films of moisture. But until
within the past two decades no way to measure this
water had been found. The scientific world had to
wait until the physicists learned to manufacture

"heavy water" as a substitute for ordinary water. Heavy water contains in each molecule a heavier kind of hydrogen, one that is rare in nature but now manufactured as a step toward releasing nuclear energy. If a known quantity of heavy water is introduced into the body, it soon spreads wherever ordinary water goes. Always it can be detected, and its concentration measured. From studies of this kind has come the knowledge that beyond the blood vessels are about fifteen quarts of water in the form of escaped plasma, and another thirty quarts are inside the cells, where it participates both as a solvent and as a raw material in the chemical reactions of life.

Since all our ancestors for at least three hundred million years have been land creatures, it seems absurd for a human being to be so wet. Yet, in the daily operation of our body, a mere three-tenths of the total weight must manage the seven-tenths that is water, moving it from place to place, making good all water losses, as well as feeding the three-tenths that does all the work. So important are the 100-odd pounds of water in a 150-pound individual that a loss of more than 10 pounds by dehydration can be fatal. So long as we have water to drink, we can endure starvation or a hunger strike for a month. But without fresh water the healthiest person will die within one to four days, depending upon the rate at which moisture is lost until the water in the body falls below the critical supply.

Although our ancestors have been terrestrial for so long, each person spends the first nine months of life almost as aquatic as any fish. Within the womb the fetus is buoyed up by a warm sea that is almost iden-

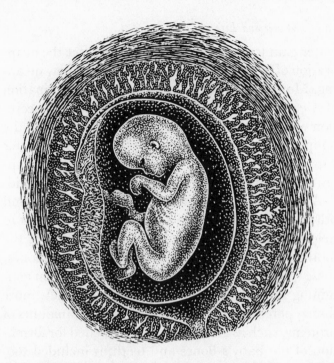

tical with blood plasma, and hence brackish—a third as rich in salts as the oceans of the Earth. At birth, the bag of waters bursts; the mother's muscles expel first the baby, then the bag. Perhaps three quarts—six pounds—of fluid drain away from around a baby that may weigh the same. They leave it stranded, exposed to inconstant temperature, to unfamiliar light, and to a world in which food, oxygen, and wastes no longer come and go neatly through the umbilical cord. From that moment on, recurrent thirst becomes second only to a need for air.

Despite the most ideal food supply, a newborn baby loses weight for the first few days. It loses water rapidly through its soft, moist skin until this covering of the body hardens, thickens and tautens. Soon these losses are reduced and more than compensated by

water gain from its liquid food. Thereafter the evaporation of water through the skin takes on new meaning. More and more the baby controls the formation
of sweat rising to the surface, and produces the secretion whenever cooling is needed to keep constant the
temperature of internal organs. Away with the water
vapor goes surplus heat—more heat per ounce evaporated than would be possible with any other liquid.

Among the strangest uses of water in mankind and
other mammals is its role in carrying nourishment to
helpless young from modified sweat glands in the
mother. Under the compulsion of her hormones,
these special glands produce a watery emulsion containing nearly 7 percent milk sugar (lactose), more
than 3 percent butter fat, and significant amounts of
proteins (such as casein). Calcium, needed for formation of the baby's bones and teeth, is included too,
far beyond the faint traces found in sweat. Yet the
mother's cells give up their important product only
when demand for it is insistent. For nearly a minute
the baby must suck vigorously before the mother's
nervous system triggers the release of still another
hormone—one causing contraction of delicate muscles within her breasts, expelling their milk into passageways leading to the baby. Between the secreting
cells and the baby, the milk gets no chance to become
contaminated or to deteriorate.

The hungry baby cries, although for the first few
weeks no watery tears spill down its cheeks. Even a
premature baby produces some tears, and they serve
their important role of washing and lubricating the
eyes, bringing nourishment to the clear cells of the
corneas, and actually destroying bacteria which

otherwise would cause infection. But this early flow of tears, like that under normal circumstances later on, is so steady and well controlled that it remains invisible. The liquid collects in the corner of the eye nearer the nose and, with every closing of the lids, is pumped into the nasal passages, where it joins the mucous film being propelled to the throat and swallowed.

Soon the distressed infant produces tears so copiously that they overflow its lids. Additional amounts we do not see are coursing through its nose, keeping its throat wet despite the extra movement of air in and out while the baby cries. If crying is important to bring attention and make the baby comfortable, tears are essential in keeping its throat moist and sanitary.

The shedding of tears, sweat, and blood have long been associated with disaster. That master of English, Sir Winston Churchill, linked them nine years before he became Britain's wartime Prime Minister. Although he was describing the defeats suffered by the armies of the Czar before the Russian Revolution, whose sweat, tears, and blood "bedewed the endless plain," he probably was aware that the three liquids of human life had been grouped in 1611 by the English clergyman and poet John Donne.

The real disaster for each individual comes when the loss of water in any form is uncompensated. Before birth, the precarious balance between too little and too much water in the body is attended to through the umbilical cord and by an occasional swallowing by the unborn babe of some warm imitation sea within the womb. From birth on, the baby's own kidneys assume the role of regulator. They let water pass or reabsorb it into the blood according to the amount of a hormone circulating there. The hormone, in turn, issues from the pituitary gland below the brain in inverse proportion to the amount of water in the blood. More water, less hormone, more water from the kidneys and less remaining in the blood—until more hormone is called forth.

After the baby's first gasp of air, water assumes still another role which must be continued for life. From the blood coursing through the lungs water emerges to form a thin, wet film lining every air-filled cavity. From solution in such a liquid film the carbon dioxide can escape and be exhaled, while oxygen dissolves and diffuses by the reverse route into the red cells for transport to all the living tissues of the body. Without the water film no gas exchange is possible between the lungs and blood. Without gas exchange, life is soon snuffed out.

The phlegm that Aristotle knew is part of a safety system protecting the vital film of moisture in the lungs. In mouth and nose, throat and windpipe are many microscopic glands that transfer water from the blood and mucus (their special secretion) into the air-filled passageways, humidifying the inhaled air until it is saturated at the temperature of the lungs. Like a warm breeze from over a tropic sea, the air can bring its life-sustaining oxygen without competing for moisture. Only on a frosty morning, when the exhaled breath chills into a cloud of water droplets, do we realize how much moisture we add to each lungful. In a hot, dry desert, this water loss becomes large enough to threaten the balance needed for survival.

Probably the ancients did not distinguish between phlegm and saliva. Indeed, until the present century and the discovery of enzymes as digestive ferments, the water and slippery mucus in saliva seemed the most important ingredients. They serve as a lubricant, making easier the act of swallowing. The mucus spreads out as an indigestible film over the inner surface of the digestive tract. If it were not for the mucus, the digestive agents in the stomach and intestine would attack the lining cells.

So inconspicuous are most digestive agents as they are secreted into the alimentary canal that the amounts proved astonishing, once they were measured: a pint of saliva daily; more than a pint of bile; still more from the pancreas; four-fifths of a quart of "gastric juice" from glands in the walls of the stomach; and three quarts from glands in the walls of the small intestine. Most of this is water, with important substances in solution. Virtually all of it is reabsorbed and returned to the blood stream by the large intestine. Over and over we use the same water, conserving the body's supply.

The greenish or yellow bile that Aristotle found is more conspicuous than the other digestive agents, because it collects in the gall bladder and there is concentrated by dehydration. A human gall bladder, when full, contains about two fluid ounces of the concentrate. His "black bile," which he supposed to cause gloomy thoughts, has no known counterpart in a live human body. It may have been imaginary, to round out the four humors, or may have been dark disintegrating blood in the spleen and kidneys of dead animals he opened long after decay had begun.

Besides water, mucus, and the pigments that give ordinary bile its color, this secretion from the liver contains soluble bile salts, which act like detergents, making water wetter. Without them, fats in the digestive tract repel water and the fat-splitting ferments it contains. But the dissolved bile salts have an affinity for fats, and form over each mass a film one molecule thick. This film allows muscular action in the walls of the digestive tract to emulsify the fat, vastly increasing the area of surface upon which the bile salts are spread. It also brings water and fat-splitting enzymes close enough to fat molecules to make their simplification possible. The products of fat digestion are smaller molecules which are soluble and absorbable, making the nourishment in the fats available to the body.

Water serves a different role in the digestion of carbohydrates. Through the activity of different enzymes, the water molecules are fitted into suitable sites in a carbohydrate molecule. Then the complex can be split in two, one half containing part of the water molecule, the other half the remainder. In this way a molecule of water is used to split a molecule of cane sugar (sucrose), which has twelve carbon atoms linked together like a chain. The products of digestion are two six-carbon sugars, one of them fruit sugar (fructose), the other grape sugar (glucose). Both are absorbed into the blood stream and carried to the liver. There the cells change the fruit sugar into grape sugar and return it to the blood. Grape sugar is "blood sugar," which goes in solution in the water of blood plasma to all cells of the body and furnishes the energy for life.

Comparatively few among the countless chemical reactions in life are like digestion in using directly the atoms of which water is composed. But all of life's chemical changes take place in watery solutions. Without water there is no life. Fortunately, both in the body and outside it, water is the most abundant liquid on earth.

So small and lightweight are the molecules of water that a fluid ounce contains a trillion trillion of them. No microscope shows particles in this range of infinitesimal size. But, by using modern techniques of extraordinary delicacy, physicists have learned the exact disposition in the tiny molecule of the one oxygen atom and two of hydrogen that the chemist has long shown by the familiar symbols H_2O or HOH. All of the strange and important characteristics of water arise from the configuration of the three atoms in the molecule and the distribution of electrical charge among them.

Each water molecule has a tetrahedral shape, like a solid bounded by four triangles. Two of the corners are vacant, one of them never even visited by an orbiting electron. The other two corners are occupied by the hydrogen atoms, each of them sharing an electron with the oxygen atom, and thereby forming a partnership of immense stability. A measure of the affinity of these two kinds of atoms for one another can be seen in the intense heat of an oxy-hydrogen flame, when a welder burns hydrogen with oxygen and forms water molecules. To separate the oxygen from its hydrogen again requires even more energy. For this reason alone the disintegration of water is an unlikely event.

The disposition of the hydrogen atoms at two corners of the tetrahedron, leaving the other two vacant, gives polarity to a water molecule and accounts for the remarkable abilities it has to serve as an almost universal solvent, for its role in forming acids and alkalis, for its great inertia to change in temperature, for the amount of heat it must absorb to evaporate, and for its strange increase in bulk upon freezing. In ice, the tetrahedral molecules form a regular latticework with a great deal of space between—more space than among the freely moving molecules of liquid water. This makes ice lighter than an equal volume of water, and lets it float. Upon thawing, the lattice collapses and the molecules that are freed fit into the spaces of the slush.

If it were not for the strong polarity of water molecules, we might escape from the one real danger caused by cold. When ice forms inside human cells, as it can do if they are exposed to freezing temperatures, the molecules align themselves so forcefully into ice needles that they are likely to puncture the cells and cause their death. Since life did not meet this hazard until it ventured far from its ancestral seas and the Tropics, perhaps it should be regarded as a small price to pay for all the versatility and benefits conferred by water.

Wherever we go, we carry within us a personal portable ocean which maintains a wet, warm environment of outstanding constancy for all of the body's cells. We may travel widely, as Thoreau boasted of doing, within a few miles of the place where we were born. We may venture far across the great expanses of land and sea and outer space. But always we must stay within reach of water distilled by the sun, falling to earth again as rain or snow. Our internal sea must never grow salty because of a loss of water to our environment. The ways of human life are fresh-water ways. Only by respecting this long-established fact can we continue to improve our hold upon the solid land.

2

WATER WAYS

ALTHOUGH man's distant kin the gorillas seem to get all the water they need in their forest homeland without drinking, the archeologists assume that, from first to last, the human species have been water drinkers, developing the earliest societies at the forest edge near streams and lakes. There, presumably, the most primitive of suspected human beings became toolmakers, and carried this skill wherever man spread throughout the ancient world.

When man became a fire tender and a fire maker, he surely learned too that water is a fire quencher. It just took him longer to letter the emergency water jar FOR FIRE ONLY, and to coin the slogan "Put out your campfire and keep the country green." Seemingly a knowledge of how to manage fire went with man on his first travels into the unknown lands far from home. It helped him soften the toughest meat and transform some ingredients of plant food into substances he could digest.

Wood for a fire is found commonly littering the banks of rivers, the shores of lakes and the coasts of major seas. Often the floodwaters and storms have broken it into pieces of convenient size, and the sun

has dried it thoroughly. Nothing could be more convenient for boiling fish or crabs or clams. For cooking
or steaming food, and for putting out the fire, salt
water is just about as good as fresh—and occasionally
better. But man could not travel merely by finding
wood and food and sea water. Unlike the ocean-
going fishes, the crabs and coastal clams, the sea birds
and porpoises and whales, he must have a daily
supply of water no more than a third as salty as the
sea. His body demands it. Although no real understanding of this limitation came until recent years,
early man sensed it. He traveled along fresh waters
for millennia before he began striking out overland
or across the salty seas.

Increasingly, the discoveries of the fossil hunters
point to eastern Africa, near or below the Equator,
for the original home of mankind. Before and during
the great Ice Ages, the rivers and fresh-water lakes
in the Rift Valley of East Africa may have channeled
human travels away from the center of man's origin.
People spread northward to the Red Sea and Asia
Minor, to the shores of the Mediterranean and the
West, to the Indian Ocean and the Far East. The
emigrants must have been farmers and ranchers, for
wherever they found the fertile flood plain of a great
river they settled. Later these became the centers of
civilizations: the Nile, the Euphrates and the Tigris,
the Indus, the Ganges and Brahmaputra, the Irra-
waddy and Salween, the Mekong, the Si-kiang, the
Yangtze, and the Hwang Ho. Many of these flood
plains grew populous and fell into chaos before the
cultures of the West got around to keeping written
records. As with the making of a diary, it is one thing

to have events to chronicle and quite another to find the time or the people to record them for posterity.

To better visualize early communities of mankind, we look today for tribesmen who live near a reliable source of water, yet use few of the trappings of civilization. Our expectations are fulfilled when we visit the pale-skinned Indians of Darien in eastern Panama, or the black-skinned Melanesians along the mountain rivers of New Guinea. In the mud near the flowing water and the forest they erect stout posts and build their houses on stilts, above the reach of ordinary floods. Often with no walls to hide this second-story life from view, these people look on all sides into the wet forest from which they get their water and some of their food. But every year the free tribesmen become scarcer, since without possessions they can offer little competition to men with firearms and keen-edged tools. Laws afford almost no protection to primitive people, for laws are made and kept —or broken—only by men with possessions.

To find tribesmen whose wealth is in intangible freedom, rather than in tangible property, it is now necessary to travel into some of the least accessible wet places on earth, or into deserts. The Indians of the lake district in Brazil's Mato Grosso have been free, but cannot long fend off their land-hungry neighbors on all sides. The people of Africa's great marsh country—the Sudd of the Sudan, far up the Nile—can hold out only until their wet land is drained and civilized. Near the headwaters of the same river, in the Ituri forests of the eastern Congo, the Pygmies may maintain a respectable independence until the ax and the bulldozer fell their refuge.

The Bushmen of the Kalahari Desert between Bech-
uanaland and South Africa, like the aborigines of
Australia, have retired into inhospitable land. Their
numbers are limited by the amount of hidden water
they can find. By remaining possessionless they can
manage with less moisture than can people with possessions. The thirst that goes with ownership is the
real, although intangible barrier safeguarding these
people of the desert.

Life for a denizen of the Mato Grosso, for a marshman of the Sudd, or a Pygmy in the Ituri forest bears
no real resemblance to Thoreau's stay by Walden
Pond. Thoreau prided himself on having built a
habitable home and stocked it for his stay at a total
expense of $28.12½, at a time when Harvard College
charged $30 a year for a student's room. Allowing for
a tenfold inflation in costs to the present time, Thoreau's admitted investment would come to $281.25.
No service a Pygmy or marshman or Mato Grossan
could perform would earn him such a fortune. Nor
was Thoreau's accounting as scrupulous as might be
asked. He did not list the Harvard education that
helped him think and write so well at Walden; or the
books and ledgers he used there in his reading and
writing; or the good meals he enjoyed in Concord at
the cost of walking to town and back. Thoreau paid
no tribute to a village chief, and went to jail rather
than yield tax money, while squatting free on land
belonging to another man. He supported no wife and
family, and left a heritage that has meaning only for
people with possessions and a feeling of being pos-
sessed by them. Thoreau came close to nature, but
not to the life of the Indians who preceded him in
Concord or of the primitives who remain today.

With the aid of an unmentioned earlier settler who cleared a bit of land near Walden Pond, and of a farmer given due credit for his work with horse and plow, Thoreau was able to raise a crop of beans and remark that "it is not necessary that a man should earn his living by the sweat of his brow, unless he sweats easier than I do." Working with his hoe, Thoreau "was determined to know beans," but he supplemented his diet with fish from the pond. Although for him the experiment in living was a success, it could not be recommended to many others. For how many other people could the waters of Walden furnish fish? How many families could the bordering woodlands supply with fuel before all the trees were cut to make a place for beans?

Forests grow only where the supply of rain or soil water is greater in every month than the amount of water that evaporates from the foliage. They cannot go dormant in warm weather, as grasses do when the supply of water fails. But even in the Tropics, a forest can support only a small human population. It is a place where man walks on the ground far below the green canopy of dominant trees, where virtually all of the leaves and flowers and fruits are spread. If the rainfall is heavy, the canopy is dense; nutrient minerals are leached rapidly from the shaded soil, until the principal place for seedlings is in the fast-rotting trunks of fallen trees, where sunlight reaches the ground. If the rainfall is less and the canopy thinner, the soil grows rich under a tangle of fallen trees and branches, each coated with inedible ferns, mosses, and lichens.

When we visited the Ituri forests, where the Pygmies live, we found the great trees in dense stands, laced together at the top with flowering vines whose ropelike stems are the lianas that reach the soil between the tree boles. Except for the kinds of trees and the presence of Pygmies, the rain forest could have been in Malaya or the basin of the Amazon or near the coast of the Caribbean in Central America. Unlike these others, the Ituri is home to the largest beetles in the world, the goliath beetles, whose grubs are eaten by the Pygmies along with whatever smaller insects, snails, and lizards they can catch. The men are expert archers, able to bring down birds and mammals that show themselves among the lower branches of the trees. From a wealth of woods and foliage these people can select the materials they need for making bows and arrows, for preparing the vegetable poison with which the arrow shafts are tipped. Nor do the men hesitate to climb high above the ground to get edible fruits. All of these needs are satisfied because the basin of the Congo gathers rain reliably from the humid easting winds.

Despite the green luxuriance, the big beetles, the high-borne crops of fruit, these densest forests of the world offer relatively little that a man can eat. Of water there is no scarcity at any season. But the Pygmies must wander continually, each group of related families in its accepted territory, to reach fresh resources within the forest tangle. Among these little people, food demands are modest and social organization is wonderfully developed. Yet they can never combine their necessarily nomadic way of life among the trees with a civilization based upon possessions.

The marshlands of the Sudd, like the Everglades

of Florida to which the Seminole Indian tribe re-
treated, support only a few more people to the square
mile than a rain forest, and at a bare subsistence level.
Too few of the marsh animals can be cropped for
food, and too little of the marsh vegetation is edible or
digestible. To the human species, marshes and dense
forests form better hiding places than living spaces.

At first, it seems paradoxical that man cannot find
as much to eat in a rain forest or a marsh as he does
along the edge of the woods or on an exposed hillside.
Surely the plants which grow in such profusion prove
that the living conditions are almost ideal: plenty of
water, of sunlight, and of soil within easy reach of
roots. But, on closer inspection, the truth emerges. A
forest or a marsh is a vegetable edifice composed
chiefly of cellulose and lignin, two complex molecules
that neither man nor most animals are able to digest.
In a rain forest or a marsh, the digestible starches and
sugars are scarce, and proteins, which are essential
foods anywhere, are even rarer. A far better measure
of the suitability of any part of the world for man is
the average weight of protein it produces per square
mile. In this respect, a rain forest or a marsh is little
better than a desert.

The hunter and the fur trapper have long known
that their greatest success lay along the edge of the
forest. More proteins and digestible foods are found
within reach there than anywhere else. Water is
plentiful all year, too, for without it there would be
no healthy growth of trees. The boundary between
the woodlands and the water may be enforced by a
sudden drop-off into cool depths, as along the shore
of a lake or a river. Or it may grade into a swamp.

Between a forest and a grassland is an even more productive edge, to which, curiously, no distinctive name has been given. Mankind probably arose along this boundary, taking advantage of the abundant rain and the wealth of food among the seedling trees. It is an unstable band of vegetation, where grassfires and then grass encroach upon the trees in dry years, and where young trees spring up in wet times, extending the forest and shading the grass out of existence.

Before man learned to make fire, he seems seldom to have stayed for long in the dense forest. Its shadows and high humidity may have made it seem a dreary place, especially on a cloudy day or a rainy night. But with fire he could drive back the forest and make more space for food plants in the sun. Since then the forest has often been chiefly a source of fuel and of logs for houses and bridges and boats. That a forest is the world's best trap for rain, doling it out from springs, keeping the rivers flowing, is a recent realization. It seems hard to learn and easy to forget. All over the world, one civilization after another has fallen when the last forests were cut, when the water table sank until crop plants died and the pasture grasses went dormant, when wells went dry and erosion carried away the soil.

Most men live today where forests once grew. Some of the most famous forests in the world have been whittled away by woodcutters, leaving devastation in their place. Today only a few hundred trees remain from the cedars of Lebanon, on the mountain slopes to which King Solomon sent "four-score thousand hewers" to get lumber for the construction and ornamentation of his temple. Beyond the one grove preserved for posterity, the slopes are bald, eroded, fit only for the few goats that prevent any accumulation of new growth. In Greece, in Italy, and in Spain, the goats and sheep have replaced the trees that preceded the civilizations of the past. In each area the normally plentiful rainfall no longer maintains steady rivers and full wells. In consequence, the people who still live there must often go long distances to get water for household use.

Daily, in food or drink, each person of adult size needs on the average about two quarts of water. Two parents and two children require at least six quarts. Following the rule that "a pint's a pound, the world around," this is twelve pounds of water each day for the most modest family. So long as a lake or a stream or a spring is within easy reach of the household, even a child may make several trips and bring home the needed liquid. But as the population grows and the water table falls, families find themselves as much as eight to twelve miles from the nearest reliable spring. In some parts of the Near East, the wife must walk ten miles with an empty jar and back ten miles with a full one—a trip that takes all day. To look after the children and the house while she is away, a man needs a second wife. In these now-arid parts of the world, the development of polygamous custom is sometimes credited to this simple problem in household logistics.

Waterfront land, of course, has all the advantages. But as with all tangible property, conflicting interests must be satisfied by some compromise. A stream or a lake is a place for the men to fish, and this activity cannot be denied whether the fishermen are there for pleasure or to get food—high-quality food, for it is

animal protein with polyunsaturated fats. Waterfront land may suit the farmer wonderfully well,
particularly if the water level rises moderately during
wet season and then subsides, leaving a fresh layer of
silt that enriches the emerging land and makes it a
suitable bed for seedlings. Crop plants and fishing
do not necessarily go together.

Land at a little distance from a fresh-water lake or
stream may be given the benefits of waterfront property if an irrigation ditch can be dug. This pattern of
land use has been polished by the people who settled
beside rivers in the East, both Near and Far. There
they grow rice, which is man's most productive cereal
crop where water is plentiful and the weather is warm.
It grows best in level paddy fields kept wet or even
flooded with fresh water. The growing grain develops
with still greater thrift if carp (or even the ornamental
variety known as goldfish) are allowed to nuzzle the
mud around the roots, where they find worms and
insects and some plant food as well. The rice grows
faster if human wastes are added to the water—a
matter of considerable convenience as well for workers
in the rice paddies. In the warm shallow ponds spread
in the sun, small snails act as scavengers, while
minute crustaceans (such as water fleas) swim fitfully
and feed on drifting types of microscopic plant life.

These conditions are perfect for rice culture, and
also for many parasites that attack man. Blood flukes
emerge from the human wastes, spend a while in the
snails, and then burrow into the exposed skin of human waders who tend the rice crop. Tapeworm eggs
hatch in the water to microscopic young, which invade the minute crustaceans dancing where fish eat
them. Man gets the tapeworm by eating fish raw.

These wading and eating habits tend to develop wherever man settles in a warm, well-watered land and eliminates the trees. Without wood for fuel, dry straw from the rice plants must be conserved for cooking the cereal, which otherwise is almost indigestible. Or for reinforcing mud bricks with which to build a woodless house. How can people with an abundance of water, of rice, and of children, but a real scarcity of fuel, be expected to boil water before drinking it, even if it brings them dysentery and blood flukes?

A corner of the paddy field may be too shallow for fish, but not for rice and mosquitoes. When the mosquitoes complete their wriggler and bullhead stages in the warm water, they transform into winged hypodermic needles which visit people. While taking a trivial amount of blood, the insects carry dangerous diseases from one victim to the next.

The degree to which large numbers of people can survive in ill health to adulthood is shown by the statistics from civilized, irrigated lower Egypt. When called up for military service at the beginning of World War II, draftees from lower Egypt proved to be so enfeebled by blood flukes and other chronic infections that most of them were unfit for induction. The Egyptian army came to consist almost entirely of men from upper Egypt, where irrigation has not yet spread rice culture into a year-round type of farming.

Today the government of Egypt is gambling the future of the whole country on the chance that a way will be found to control blood flukes and other diseases associated with continuous irrigation in a warm climate. The odds are poor and the facts are known, for in 1963 the Ministry of Health estimated that about twelve million out of twenty-seven million people were suffering seriously from blood flukes alone. But the grave risk in building the new Aswan Dam is politically more expedient than a return to the old way of using the Nile, which worked for more than six thousand years—but supported fewer, healthier people.

Originally the river flooded its broad plain each summer. Thousands of families withdrew to the shores above high water. Then they followed the ebbing flood, planting their rice and other vegetables on the exposed mud. Their crop grew as the soil dried out, and they harvested it all before the waters of the Nile spread again from its springtime channel. Through the growing season, neither the mosquitoes that carry malaria nor the fresh-water snails that are an essential link in the life history of a blood fluke had a place to live when people tended their drying fields along the Nile.

Later the Egyptians built levees along the spring-time channel and great dikes of earth. When the Nile flooded, the muddy water was allowed to flow through gates in the levees and dikes, filling a whole system of irrigation basins. As before, it brought to the land a fertilizing silt from the Blue Nile and the mountainous country of Ethiopia, and organic matter from the marshes of the Sudd, flushed out by meltwater and rain from the White Nile, drained from the Ruwenzori Range in the eastern Congo. The system of levees and dikes merely slowed the fall of the flood waters on the irrigated fields, and kept the hot sun from drying out the soil so quickly, reducing the yield of the crops.

Excess silt still settled in the main channel of the Nile, and built up its bed until each flood threatened to overflow the levees. To safeguard their earthworks, the Egyptians constructed overflow basins such as ancient Lake Moeris, near Al Fayyum. Century after century, with a few exceptions when the Nile failed to flood or rose too high, this amount of management of its waters supported the Egyptian economy. The Pharaohs came and went. So did Alexander the Great, and Caesar, and Mohammed, and the Crusaders, and Napoleon. Other cultures rose and fell, but still the agriculture along the flood plain of the Nile went on.

Along the levees that paralleled the river's channel, water could be pumped in various ways to irrigate fields nearby and double the yield of crops. To make these advantages more general, engineers of the nineteenth century devised earthen barrages behind which flood waters could be impounded to be used for irrigation throughout the year in lower Egypt. In 1902 a small dam was built at Aswan, to further hold the river in check and divert its flow in the dry winter season into canals feeding irrigation projects lower down. Land well beyond the flood basin could then be brought under cultivation. Flooding was minimized, and crop failure became virtually unknown. But no longer was a fertilizing layer of silt spread annually over the fields, or were the excess salts carried back to the river by its slowly receding waters. No longer did the soil dry out after its one crop was harvested, to be aerated, warmed and sterilized. Instead, crops and mosquitoes and snails could thrive all year—except that the soil grew waterlogged, requiring expensive drainage ditches; and salty from continuous evaporation, unless flushed out with extra water; and deficient in many important minerals, if fertilizer was not added, bought from the sale of the extra crops. These were the changes that led to the sad state of health in lower Egypt at the beginning of World War II.

When the high dam now under construction at Aswan is completed, a reservoir 162 miles long in upper Egypt will fill and furnish irrigation water continuously for more than 3,000 square miles of land that until now has been useless. Parasitologists are fearful that this change will lead immediately to a severe deterioration of health in the remainder of the country, as a high price for progress and more food. Engineers who ignore the threat of blood flukes and malaria are more concerned about the amount of water that will evaporate from the new reservoir. The residue will contain a higher concentration of salts than is ideal in irrigation water. It will become still more concentrated while flowing for a thousand miles in man-made ditches all the way to the Mediterranean Sea. That the lower Nile, which for centuries has served as a corridor for commerce below Aswan, may contain too little water to be navigable because of the new diversions, seems to the Egyptians a small price to pay for more food.

Fresh water can be used as a highway for travel in boats, and for transport of produce on its way to market, without much change in the amount or quality of the water. Lakes and navigable rivers have always provided the first highway system into each new land. Long before the shores are colonized for agriculture or lined with rows of habitations, the waterways finger between the forest trees and give access to a wide area. The flowing and standing waters of America were mapped and traveled by the fur traders long before any civilized man ventured overland to explore beyond the drainage basins. The person who traces a river to its farthest source rates a more secure place in history than the man who finds the center of a forest, a prairie, or a desert.

Some historians claim that, wherever a civilization developed along the banks of a long, broad, tranquil river, invention led to possession of ships suitable for crossing minor seas or exploring the coasts of major oceans. From the Egyptian barges with their long rows of oarsmen and lateen-rigged sails, the Phoenicians of Asia Minor are credited with developing still better models with which to trade along Mediterranean shores. Perhaps the civilization that reached an early climax and then fell on the island of Crete arose through adoption of earlier models of the same Nile River craft.

In riding the salt waters of the Mediterranean and extending first commerce and then civilization around that land-encircled sea, the sailors and oarsmen depended upon fresh water and food obtained ashore. By staying within sight of land, they retained a sense of security from thirst and starvation. They ran the risk of foundering on shoals, or of being swept helplessly into unknown waters by sudden storms. All of these hazards found their way into classic literature, and were retold endlessly in the *Aeneid* and the *Odyssey*. Yet these tales could stem from memorable single events rather than repeated happenings. For

much of the time the waters of the Mediterranean are
calm, and the shiploads of healthy merchants and
warriors may have feared more perils than they met.
An uneventful journey makes no news at home.

The real odysseys went unrecorded. They were
undertaken by the early inhabitants of Malaya, who
began traveling by outrigger canoe from island to
island in the East Indies, and finally as far as New
Zealand. To cross the Mediterranean at its widest
point is only half as far as to New Zealand from the
nearest bit of land.

Whether traveling from one fresh-water spring to
the next in an arid part of a continent, or from an
island with fresh water to the next that is similarly
blessed, mankind travels from oasis to oasis. He must
have fresh water or perish along the way. The African
Bushman knows this, and carries several ostrich-egg
shells filled with water to keep him alive while he
crosses the Kalahari Desert. The Bedouins who brave
the fringes of the great Sahara know it, and load their
camels with sheepskins filled with the precious liquid.
The intrepid navigators of canoes among the islands
of the Pacific know it. But their solution to the need
for water requires the product of a coastal tree that is
widespread only in the Tropics. Into the canoe they
toss a few dozen green coconuts. Whenever thirsty,
they open one of these giant fruits and satisfy themselves with the pleasant, untainted "milk" the husk
and shell protect.

Among the tools of mankind, the coconut and the
ostrich-egg shell and mammal-skin bag are seldom
listed. Yet they made travel possible long before the
invention of the clay pot, the glass jar, the steel drum,

and the plastic container. The canteen fastened to the belt of doughboys in World War I or of Boy Scouts setting off on a hike are much later aids with the same aim. So is the cloth water bag dripping on the outside of a car crossing our southwestern deserts in summer. All of them are cultural ways in which the human species has dodged the dangers in a dry world, ways that have evolved far faster than any changes in the chemistry of survival to be found in other living things.

The ingenuity of man is turned today toward new ways to have fresh water available constantly while he travels. Gone is the mariner's old-time trust in water casks on deck; it vanished along with his reliance upon a favorable wind to fill his sails. To cross the ocean, a modern ship may leave port with less than a day's supply of fresh water per person aboard. Salt water, of course, can be used to wash down the decks, to flush the toilets, and to quench any fire at sea. Yet, barring a breakdown, no shortages are probable for drinking, washing, or cooking. Like the pitcher of Baucis and Philemon, the tanks of fresh water remain full despite a rate of withdrawal that seems excessive. Aboard the S. S. *Independence*, the 1,600 passengers and crew use daily about 500 tons (120,000 gallons) of fresh water, from stainless tanks that hold only 400 tons. This paradox is possible because heat released from fuel oil continues to free moisture by distillation from the sea itself, and to pump pure water into the storage reservoirs.

The newest need is for containers that can yield their burden of fresh water without spilling under conditions of weightlessness. Thirst is now sensed in a hurtling capsule circuiting the globe every 85 minutes. But it was the old cry of the Ancient Mariner: "Water, water, every where,/Nor any drop to drink" that came from astronaut Gordon Cooper, cocooned within the *Faith 7*. To anxious earthlings hundreds of miles below him he radioed a description of his predicament. His plastic tubes of drinking water, which were designed to be squeezed like toothpaste, had not yielded their contents as planned, and now were empty. In the cabin air before his eyes hung weightless drops of water. But he could not capture enough of them with a handkerchief to slake his growing thirst. Since so few more circuits had to be made before he ended his flight, his situation was far from desperate. But future astronauts, on longer journeys, must have better containers for fresh water as they go exploring to distant worlds, at speeds that let man's body catch up with his imagination.

3

TILL THE WELL RUNS DRY

AMONG the promises recorded in the book of Exodus under Moses' direction is a bargain: in return for serving the Lord, "he shall bless thy bread, and thy water." Today these two commodities are viewed differently in the Poor Nations and the Rich Nations. In the one, a sufficiency of water and of bread has become a dream. In the other, they are the bare necessities of life—the fare for someone who may be denied all other benefits of his society.

Water actually satisfies more different human wants than does any other natural resource. But of these many needs, virtually all are met best by fresh water; most are exclusively so. Yet, at any moment, the supply of fresh water is limited. Constantly it is replenished, distilled from the oceans by solar energy and distributed by the sun-powered winds. According to Dr. Roger Revelle, director of the Scripps Institute of Oceanography, about a fourth of the energy the earth gets from the sun goes into evaporating sea water; this is still nearly 10,000 times as much power as man manages altogether. Despite annual fluctuations related to sunspots and solar flares, producing wet years on earth and dry ones, the pattern of evaporation and of winds that transport the vapor remains almost as constant as the sites and shapes of the continents, the heights and the slopes of their mountain chains.

Every day the sun penetrates the clouds in the earth's atmosphere and warms the surface waters of the oceans. Yet, after the rains at sea have cleared the air, only an eighth of the total water that evaporated is left to ride the winds beyond the shores and over the land. There it enters into endless convections of moisture which are of the utmost importance to people. Of the precipitation that man measures with his rain gauges on every continent and island, an average of 61 percent evaporates again from the soil, from the vegetation, and from the surface of inland waters. The remainder, which flows seaward down the rivers and through subterranean streams, completes the great cycle. It is the same 24 cubic miles of water, blown inland daily, freshening the continents and leveling them by erosion.

In seeking fresh water to satisfy his many needs, man looks to the rain on land. He sees an enormous total. On the 36 billion acres of continents and islands, a yearly average of 26.3 inches drops from the clouds or condenses as dew. The hydraulic engineer, who is a specialist at gathering and channeling water for human use, measures all this precipitation in acre-feet—a foot depth on an acre of area—each acre-foot being 325,872 gallons. The world's annual rainfall on land totals 82 billion acre-feet, which is enough to satisfy the thirst of 1,780 people per acre. If all this rain and snow could be collected and kept pure enough to drink, it would be plenty for a human population of 146 trillion.

So great a population—one person for every 25 square feet of land surface—is no longer beyond imagination, although it is close to the "standing room only" that has been predicted. With 2,400 million people counted by the Statistical Office of the United Nations in 1950 and 3,115 millions in mid-1962, the rate of doubling justifies a prediction of 7,000 million people in A.D. 2000. A continuation of this rate for three more centuries would bring the total to more than 146 trillion in the year 2300. All the fresh water in the world—from the top of Mount Everest, the center of Antarctica, and the Greenland ice cap, as well as the vast basins of the Amazon and the Congo—would not then suffice to stave off a desperate water famine.

Shortages of fresh water for city dwellers are not uncommon today. Many a New Yorker recalls the attempts to conserve water in 1949, which was a dry year just before another reservoir was completed and a new drainage basin tapped to slake metropolitan thirst. The 1,698,000 people who live on the island of Manhattan make little use of the water that falls on their rooftops and streets. It comes at the rate of 42 inches a year, which is well above the world average of 26.3 inches. These people, who number 85 to the acre of Manhattan, rely instead upon man-made underground rivers from less populous areas upstate where water is collected.

Even with reservoirs with a capacity of 61,000 gallons per person in New York City, the commissioners on the Board of Water Supply grew alarmed on June 27, 1963. On that hot day, the citizens drew 1,648 million gallons from the mains—211 gallons apiece. This was 44 gallons per person more than the

rate that is now regarded as a normal average for
June, based upon experience in 1962 and 1963. Part
of the extra water gushed full blast from fire hydrants
that had been opened illegally to cool off children
playing in the streets. But the amount in the reservoirs, which were already low owing to six months
with less rain than usual, sank to less than two-thirds
of capacity.

A modern city can be in trouble even with double
the rainfall—84 inches a year, which is three times
the world average—if its population grows faster
than its water-collecting system. The 3,200,000 people
on the island of Hong Kong today live in one of the
wettest parts of the world. On the island they have
391 square miles of space, and are served by an
elaborate rain-catching system that hoards water in
great reservoirs. But ever since the first reservoir was
completed about a century ago the city has grown
faster than its public-works engineers could match.
In May of 1963 the distribution of water into the
mains was reduced to four hours on alternate days.
When this form of dole failed to halt the sinking
water level in the reservoirs, the rate changed in June
to three hours every fourth day. Plans were rushed to
bring in 20,000 tons of water daily from Canton in
southern China and, if necessary, to issue ration cards
for drinking water in July. In normal years, about
two-thirds of the annual rainfall comes in May
through September. But, even when all reservoirs are
filled, the total capacity is barely enough to sustain
16 people to the acre until the rains come again.

Rationing of fresh water has become the accepted
pattern in Mexico City, where the annual rainfall is

over 29 inches—still above the average for the world. The radiating water mains which serve the 4,829,000 people (132 to the acre) are divided into twelve zones, each of which receives water for two hours a day. During those hours, the pressure raises water into rooftop barrels until they are full. Those two barrels per household contain 84 gallons, and must serve until the next period when water becomes available. It takes 40 gallons to fill an ordinary bathtub to a depth of 8 inches, and 4 gallons to flush a toilet. In the face of a water shortage, there is a world of difference between owning these bathroom fittings and using them at the rate New Yorkers did even during the dry season of 1949.

Clearly, the first call on fresh water is to slake thirst. But the half gallon taken daily in wet foods and drink is trivial when compared to the gallons needed to support the most modern way of life. For slaking thirst and for washing people and clothes, dishes and automobiles, for waste disposal, for fire fighting and central air-conditioning, an average urban community in the United States uses about 158 gallons of water per person each day. European cities, whose residents long to match the American way of life, get along with about 40 gallons per person per day. If all the people in the world were suddenly to adopt the living habits met in most American cities, the global supply of fresh water would be adequate for 158 gallons per person daily to 21.7 billion people. This many could easily be present less than a century from now.

To enjoy such cleanliness, safety from fire, and comfort when the sun is hot, the world's population needs food as well. In the United States, for every gallon of fresh water used in country homes and municipal supplies, more than 4 gallons are used to supplement natural rainfall where food is raised. The volume of water for each person to be clean, safe, comfortable, and well-fed in the average American mode is not 158 but 891 gallons a day. The human population that could enjoy this way of life would be 8.2 billions—if all the world's rain were put to this single use, without reuse. Such a population is expected during the next fifty years.

To raise food on land, people must set aside both the necessary acres and the water the crops need for successful growth. In different parts of the world, the availability of water and the food preferences of the people go hand in hand. Both influence the size of population the region can support. If the food must be beef, it takes 10 acres of land efficiently managed to raise enough to feed one person for a year. If the food can be wheat, the same 10 acres may yield instead 37,150 pounds—enough to nourish 14.8 people. Ten acres of paddy fields in the Far East can produce as much as 53,680 pounds of polished rice. This is enough to sustain 23.9 people on the diet to which they were accustomed. But only where water is abundant and fresh can a dense population get rice in this way. A minor drought, which leaves plenty of water for drinking and cooking, may still lead to relative failure of the rice harvest and fatal starvation.

If well-fed people include among the necessities of life the various kinds of agricultural machinery or automobiles, modern buildings to heat and cool, gasoline and fuel oil, electric generators and transmission lines (and the appliances we quickly accept as "essential" to civilized living), an even greater use of water must be made. To keep costs down, this water for industry must be fresh and noncorrosive. But the quantity per person rises quickly, from 819 to 1,500 gallons a day. And with the rise the number of people that the world's fresh-water supplies will accommodate without reuse drops to 4.9 billions, which is the number anticipated in 1985. With any luck at all, toddlers now in diapers will come of legal age just as this problem of supply is met head-on.

It takes water to make a diaper, as well as to wet and wash one. Every barrel of gasoline or of beer represents between 350 and 470 gallons of fresh water. To refine a ton of sugar takes 1,000 gallons of really pure water. A ton of paper emerges from manufacturing processes needing 65,000 gallons of fresh water with moderate purity; in 1960 the United States produced 4 million tons of newsprint and sanitary tissue alone. The two-thirds of a ton of steel that go into each ordinary automobile require about 44,000 gallons of fresh water; this is almost 400 trillion gallons by the time the auto makers have turned out the usual 5 million passenger cars in a year.

With a rising standard of living, more people anticipate enjoying the products of industry. On this basis it is predicted that by 1975 the daily fresh-water requirements per person in America will rise to 2,000 gallons. Use of fresh water and the advance of civilization go hand in hand. But, barring a calamity or a miracle, the world population will pass 3,650 millions by 1970, when the supply of water from the skies would provide exactly 2,000 gallons per day per person. By 1975 there will not be enough for this democratic distribution.

None of these simple computations makes a place for wild plants and wild animals. Yet the sun has never shone for mankind and our cultivated foods alone. Nor has the rain fallen and the world turned solely for human benefit. Each year, however, man takes a larger share and claims it as his right. So far this has had only modest effects on other kinds of life, mostly because engineering feats have nowhere come close to capturing and hoarding all of the rain that falls. On a limited number of islands, where natural traps for moisture and constant springs do not suffice for the human population, great hillsides have been cleared of people and cemented over to make catchments draining into subterranean cisterns. Rain that falls on a city's roofs may be similarly treasured. In hilly Hong Kong, as in flat Barbados in the West Indies, or in the Virgin Islands or Bermuda, fresh water is hard enough to get for these extreme measures to be used.

Elsewhere, it has seemed impractical to capture all of the rain and put it to human use, even on small areas. Where lush tropical forests grow, the daily rains often drop as much as two hundred inches annually. This vastly exceeds man's demonstrated ability to hoard and use the liquid efficiently. Wherever water is so abundant, it loses much of its importance in long-range plans. At the other extreme, on deserts and tundras where the rainfall annually fails to reach a total of ten inches and comes at long, irregular intervals, the supply is not worth the engineering feats needed to collect it.

Wherever man has taken trouble to divert really large quantities of fresh water to his own uses, he has generally ignored the 62.5 cubic miles a day that fall on the continents, because 38.5 cubic miles of it is lost so quickly to evaporation. He has concentrated, instead, on the 24 cubic miles that remain in flowing rivers and subterranean streams. Or he has dipped into the underground reserves—vast buried lakes that fill the spaces between mineral particles far below even some of the driest deserts. These are the fresh "waters of the earth, and the waters that are under the earth." Together they may represent as much as the total rainfall for three years on the land areas of the globe.

Only in the last few decades and in the arid southwestern states has any determined effort been made to mine the "white gold" of buried water, and to remove it faster than precipitation recharged the unseen reservoirs. Elsewhere over the industrialized United States, the needs for water have been met by taking about 14 percent of the water running over the surface on its way to the sea. If all the rivers of the world were used at a corresponding rate, they would daily supply 1,500 gallons of fresh water without re-use to about 685 million people. The human population of the world has exceeded this number ever since 1700, near the beginning of the Industrial Revolution. That the needs of so many people have been satisfied in the intervening years without greater utilization of the total supply has come through their willingness to use water over and over again. With each reuse, the water is less fresh than it was before.

When Rowland Howard wrote that "you never

miss the water till the well runs dry," he was referring to those favored parts of the world where an abundance of water can usually be counted on. These familiar lands are far less extensive than is believed by people who live in Anglo-America or in Europe. Real drought rarely comes to the eastern three-fifths of settled Canada and the United States, or to most of Europe. As in eastern China, and the northern and eastern fringes of Australia, and much of Africa south of the great deserts, and some parts of South America, the rainfall in these parts of the world ranges between twenty and sixty inches. It is enough to support an almost continuous forest. Now that man has felled the trees, the annual rains still come and water his crops and cities. But, as the song tells of Spain, they come mainly in the man-made plains.

Less than twenty inches of rain fall each year on most of Asia and Australia, much of Africa, and many parts of both Americas. Often the full quota comes in one or two torrential storms. Happy is he who chances to be in the right place at the proper moment to witness a rainbow arching above the desert or the endless prairie, where only the erosion pattern gives evidence of earlier storms. Before the rainbow fades, the accumulated rain rushes over the sunbaked ground. Most of the bonanza soon floods down the slopes, scours for an hour or two through washes that previously were bonedry, and spreads out where evaporation and seepage obliterate all signs of moisture.

At first glance it seems incredible that so thirsty a land should not profit more from a sudden storm. But the ground lacks the protection of foliage and decaying vegetation that might cushion the impact of falling raindrops. The pelting water hammers on the surface, tamping it tightly at the same time that fine particles are torn free and washed along. Some of them settle into minute crannies, closing the soil still more to entry of rain. Even where the bottom of a once-muddy lake has cracked open widely, a few gallons of water fill the cracks and the soil swells, closing these avenues to entry of further moisture. Under a hot sun, the cracks reappear again in a few days, and release water vapor from deep down in the drying soil.

Although the annual rainfall in the conterminous United States is often cited as averaging about thirty inches, the distribution of water is uneven. The seventeen western states, which constitute about 60 percent of the land area, receive only about a fourth of the water. The twenty-one eastern states, with only 40 percent of the land, get more moisture than they need. Until the present century, the distribution of people and of water-demanding crops matched rather well the distribution of water. But now, increasing numbers of citizens are choosing to live where the sun beams down and the winters are mild. To provide these people with water and let them enjoy life in the modern mode requires drastic redistribution of the country's rain. Food growers, too, have seen profits in farming the southwestern deserts because the land is cheap and fertile when irrigated, and the crops mature in off seasons when the market price is high enough to cover the cost of shipment to coastal cities.

Among rivers that flow through desert regions and make a civilization possible in the midst of arid lands,

the Nile and our own Colorado River stand out. Both rise in snowfields on spectacular mountains, the cloud-girt Ruwenzoris in Equatorial Africa and the highest Rockies along the continental divide in North America. Both rivers begin in water that soaks an alpine tundra, and both descend quickly from more than fourteen thousand feet elevation to channels through the midst of the desert.

Before the Colorado River has gone ten miles, its path is blocked by a great dam holding the Green Mountain Reservoir, from which Denver gets its water. The town of Dillon is being relocated to make space for another retaining basin, from which water will flow twenty-three miles through a great tunnel to satisfy the needs of Denver residents, even though their numbers should increase to a million. The city relies almost entirely on this source of water from the opposite side of the mountain range, and, if access to it were cut off, at least half of Denver's present 494,000 people would have to leave. Those who remained would need to rehabilitate the waters of the South Platte, which is now a polluted, depleted, unusable tributary of the Mississippi.

The second dam on the Colorado is at Palisades, near Grand Junction. It serves as much to produce electric power for about 275,000 people as to irrigate nearly 84,000 acres of alfalfa, corn, and peach orchards in the Grand River Valley, part of which is in Colorado and the rest in Utah. Beyond this, the river is a lonely one. It winds southwesterly for almost nine hundred miles through inaccessible canyons. Past Arches National Monument, it picks up water from Wyoming in the Green River, then some more from Utah in the Dirty Devil River and, as it flows into Arizona, gathers waters from New Mexico where the San Juan flows past Rainbow Bridge National Monument.

For years the educated Navajos, representing the largest Indian tribe in the United States, have wondered why their people must haul water by the barrel or two from temporary waterholes, subsisting in the portable communities characteristic of nomads who inhabit arid lands. At the bottom of the canyons, 17,000 gallons a second rush past their tribal reserves, sometimes within sight but always beyond reach. The Navajo Dam, now being constructed on the San

Juan, is intended to correct this and furnish irrigation water to the reserve in eastern Utah and Arizona along the common border. The Glen Canyon Dam, keystone of the Upper Colorado water project, is 700 feet high; it will form a lake 185 miles long on the same border. Both dams will allow electrification of an area that has long been among the most primitive in the country.

Past Lees Ferry the Colorado River flows on into its Lower Basin, through Marble Canyon, to twist into its most famous product—the Grand Canyon of the Colorado—where the rushing, turbid river is a mile below the rim rocks in an eroded chasm fourteen miles across. Only in a tributary canyon within the boundary of Grand Canyon National Park have the simultaneous presence of fresh water and usable soil allowed people to live close to the river, where the Havasupai tribe occupy a secluded spot.

Still descending twelve feet in each mile and carrying tons of sediment, the Colorado plunges onward into the calm waters of Lake Mead, along the boundary of Nevada. All of it goes through the turbines that provide electric power to an area 400 miles across, then southward to the boundary of California. There a tremendous pumping station lifts a billion gallons a day into an aqueduct 242 miles long. It provides all the water for San Diego and about a fifth of that used by the sprawling metropolis of Los Angeles. For 84 miles the aqueduct is buried in desert sand; for 93 miles it penetrates a wall of mountain rock; finally it stretches as a concrete-lined ditch to the distant destination. The whole aqueduct cost half a billion dollars—more than Hoover Dam at Lake Mead, which, until 1955, was the largest man-made reservoir in the world.

Close to Yuma, Arizona takes irrigation water from the Colorado. It travels to 115,000 acres of cropland, the Welton-Mohawk area, past sand dunes more closely resembling the driest parts of the Sahara than any other dunes within five thousand miles of Hollywood. At essentially the same point along the common boundary with California, a large proportion of the river is pumped out and sent to the Imperial Valley, the Coachella and Palo Verde irrigation districts, which have been described correctly as the nation's biggest vegetable garden. Gravity carries some of the water into the Salton Sink, where it evaporates. Most of the rest is shipped out in fruit and truck crops as their inner juices.

Beyond Arizona and California, the Colorado River supposedly has ninety miles to flow through Mexico before emptying into the Gulf of California. A treaty signed in 1944 guarantees that at least 12 percent of the water in the Colorado is to go in usable condition past the international border. Less than five miles beyond is the Morales Dam, where the Mexicans turn their residual share into the Alamo Canal, which, for all practical purposes, *is* the river beyond this point.

Along the five channels of the canal, people have built shack towns. They wash themselves and their clothes at the canal edges and haul water by the canful for drinking, cooking, and making adobe brick. But so sluggish is the flow that it no longer makes possible much use of the land in Mexico. Twice a year, in fact, tides in the Gulf of California rise high enough to push water up the canal channels. It overflows the dikes into the Mexican croplands, and leaves them too salty for growth of man's crop plants. Twice a year these flooded farms are now visited by migratory waterfowl which find food among the weeds, and by hunters who come to get the birds.

The Colorado River, which starts out so cold and pure and sparkling, takes water from seven states and contributes to three. All three, particularly California, would like more from it. So would Mexico. They want its water clean, but are unprepared to pay for cleansing it after they use it. Los Angeles, which has clamored for a larger share, still throws away 250 million gallons a day rather than reclaim the water that carries sewage into the Pacific Ocean. The hydraulic engineers want more in their irrigation canals, much of it to flush from the soil the accumulating traces of salts left behind by rapid evaporation. The price of keeping irrigated crops growing in the desert soil of the Welton-Mohawk area is repeated washing. But this alters the nature of the river until, where its waters enter Mexico, they have become three times as salty as the treaty allows. The Mexican government protests that the 12 percent residue of the Colorado River crossing the border is scarcely more useful to agriculture than brine from the Gulf of California or the open Pacific Ocean. Actually, the river is now a seventh as salty as sea water. But demineralizing it would be enormously expensive—more per year than the annual value of all the crops irrigated by the river.

The Colorado, more than most rivers, is used to the last flowing drop. It supports as many people as does the Nile, which exceeds the Colorado manyfold in volume, length, and area of drainage basin. The civilization sustained by the Colorado is also at a much higher average level. So vital, in fact, are its waters in the three principal states that share it that each has been energetic to establish legal rights to continue doing so. This vigorous jockeying for ownership of water rights led the Supreme Court of the United States to rule on the subject, giving a verdict in June, 1963.

Water rights in the various states follow two divergent policies. The eastern states (and, to a limited extent, California as well) respect "riparian law," which allots a reasonable proportion of any flowing water to the person or public agency that owns land along the water's edge. In cases of competition, the last person to have his share reduced is the one who holds priority in using water from the river. "First in time, first in right" is the slogan form of riparian law. However, no clear definition of "reasonable" seems evident, unless it is that enough water must be left in the river to cover the fishes there.

The western states (and, to a large extent, California too) follow a different rule. They respect "appropriation and beneficial use" even if the user is some distance from the river. This means essentially that the first person or agency to divert river water into his property takes all he can possibly manage, and then uses it lavishly as a guarantee of his future right to this amount.

The U. S. Supreme Court implicitly rejected the appropriation doctrine and divided the Colorado's waters anew. Half of the river's flow was reserved to the Upper Basin states (Colorado, New Mexico, Utah, and Wyoming), of which only Colorado takes any appreciable amount. In the same ruling, the Court divided the remaining half of the annual flow on the assumption that it totaled 7,500,000 acre-feet: 4,400,000 to California, 2,800,000 to Arizona, and 300,000 to Nevada. This ends the dispute between California, which has been appropriating 5,100,000 acre-feet and claiming 1,000,000 more on the basis of prior rights, and Arizona, which has diverted 1,400,000 acre-feet annually in recent years. Nevada has yet to use any large quantity, but may need to.

The 1963 change in the rules governing the Colorado River as a supply of fresh water requires no sudden alteration in the pattern of use, since the states of the Upper Basin have not completed facilities for withdrawing their allotment. However, Californians suspect that the amount of water reaching the Lower Basin may often fall to 6,000,000 acre-feet, of which California's share would then drop to 3,500,000. This would be little more than half as much as the state is now withdrawing from the Colorado every year.

The sprawling cities along the Pacific Coast and the agricultural activities in the nation's vegetable garden might manage currently with even less than 3,500,000 acre-feet if a few of the known ways to save water were put in operation. It seems easier to weigh the relative merits of different architectural styles of dams or to calculate how many million acre-feet of extra water might be brought from a distant place than to consider costs. By the time Colorado River water reaches the city limits of Los Angeles, the Metropolitan Water District of Southern California charges for it a wholesale price of $25 an acre-foot. Some of it is sold again promptly for irrigation at $14.25, subsidizing the farmers. Much of the remainder is softened at a cost of $8 per acre-foot, and sold in the treated form at $29. Water that could be saved by thrifty practice would cost almost nothing.

As though it would be a catastrophe to require frugal ways, California is building a great aqueduct from the Feather River in the wet northern part of the state. By 1972 this pipeline is expected to be in operation, bringing to Los Angeles and San Diego about 1,800,000 acre-feet a year from as far away as Chicago is from New Orleans. A price of $60 to $78 per acre-foot has been estimated conservatively for the new supply. Until it begins to flow through the aqueduct, this water will continue to run unused by man from north of Sacramento to the Pacific Ocean.

Arizona, too, is ready with plans that may save the day for Phoenix and Tucson. These two cities in the desert have been unable to manage on the water they can withdraw from the Gila River and its tributaries, and have been haunted by the possibility that California might win its claim to almost all of the water passing in the Colorado. Now the Supreme Court has guaranteed a share large enough to make worthwhile the building of a new dam in Bridge Canyon, to divert water into a "Central Arizona Project." About a fifth of this water could go to urban supplies serving nearly three-fourths of the state's population, while the remainder could irrigate farmland. Completion of the billion-dollar project might coincide closely with the new self-sufficiency of California, based on its Feather River aqueduct.

Such elaborate scheming over water is relatively new in America. It comes while unplanned adjustments are being made among competitors for fresh water from the Colorado River. As more people move into the Southwest, enjoying their freedom to work and live where they choose, the irrigated orchards of peaches and apricots, date palms and avocados are being subdivided into housing developments. Even with a few swimming pools, the nonindustrial suburbs use far less water than fields of irrigated crops. The farmers move first into outlying areas. Some of them spend as much as $60,000 for a well and a pump that will reach subterranean water, and line new irrigation ditches with concrete at a dollar a foot to prevent leakage and loss. But when many farmers mine for the same water, its level sinks as much as ten feet a year. Soon it is out of reach. The cropland must be abandoned if no other source of water can be found. Ground water is a capital asset, and cannot long be spent faster than rain regenerates the supply.

Although food comes close behind oxygen to breathe and water to drink as a necessity for human life, the food growers who need water cannot compete economically with the industrial cities for the quantities they need for irrigation. If further growth of communities in Southern California brings about a water shortage despite the aqueducts from the north and east, the coastal cities can easily outbid the farmers for the moisture all of them need. Time may be running out for agriculture in the Imperial Valley. An irrigated field may become outmoded—too expensive even to subsidize. Perhaps it is better to spend money shipping food from croplands in well-watered areas, rather than try to reroute water into the sunny deserts where so many people now choose to live.

The civic planners in some of the southwestern states have begun a new procedure that makes ranchers and farmers still more apprehensive. Lubbock, Texas, is one city where the annual rainfall averages less than twenty inches. To insure an adequate supply of muncipal water despite any foreseeable expansion of the community, the commissioners have bought up small areas of sandy property far beyond the city limits. In each of these they have drilled a deep well and reached a generous source of water. In some cases, the connecting mains have been installed. But,

THE GREAT WATER CYCLE

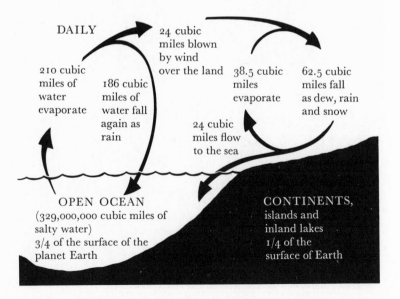

DAILY

24 cubic miles blown by wind over the land

210 cubic miles of water evaporate

186 cubic miles of water fall again as rain

38.5 cubic miles evaporate

62.5 cubic miles fall as dew, rain and snow

24 cubic miles flow to the sea

OPEN OCEAN
(329,000,000 cubic miles of salty water)
3/4 of the surface of the planet Earth

CONTINENTS,
islands and inland lakes
1/4 of the surface of Earth

since the need for the water is yet to come, these new wells remain inactive. They are insurance for the future. If a severe drought comes, every well can be activated quickly. The community, of course, would have first call on the water, even though taking it would drain the underground supplies for the ranchers and farmers on all sides. Agricultural uses of semi-arid land seem likely to become ever more marginal and hazardous.

Real rivalry for fresh water from a limited supply, as seen today chiefly in the American Southwest, portends the future in many other parts of the world. As the number of people increases and demands are made for a rising standard of living, attention will be focused firmly on the liquid bounty from the sky, upon the hills and the mountains that help man get the precious water.

4

DILUTION IS NO SOLUTION

In Paris a special meeting of experts convened in February, 1963. Before it, M. René Maheu, Acting Director-General of the United Nations Educational, Scientific and Cultural Organization (UNESCO), expressed his concern over the dwindling proportion of the world's population now served by piped supplies of water. Less than 10 percent of the 3,115 million people on earth have piped water, he pointed out, and "a good many of these have it for only a few hours each day." Although urban populations are better served, with water mains to about 30 percent, cities are growing faster than their water facilities. He called for an emergency program to find a solution to the world's "alarming and widespread shortage of water, whether for urban, industrial or agricultural" uses.

Challenging the committee members was a 1962 report from the World Health Organization (WHO). It emphasized the special plight of Central and South America, where 33 million city dwellers—nearly 40 percent of the population—have no water from a community supply; it stated that most Latin American cities lack adequate sewage facilities. Not only

59

does this hamper the industrial development that is basic to improving the standard of living, but it requires expenditure of about 15 percent of the national income to pay for disability among the gainfully employed—chiefly for gastrointestinal and contagious diseases which are virtually absent in Anglo-America and Europe. Yet, by 1980, the population of Latin America is expected to exceed by nearly 80 million the number of people in the United States. The situation in Asia is similar, and sinister.

Of the 300 million people in the world who now have a piped supply of water, more than half live in the United States. Unfortunately, the water mains serving 100 million of these come from lakes and rivers into which 120 million people and countless industrial enterprises empty their sewage.

It is no accident that the six largest cities in Anglo-America (New York, Chicago, Los Angeles, Philadelphia, Detroit, and Montreal) are all on the coast or on large bodies of water. The port facilities each enjoys are minor compared to the importance of a convenient sink for vast amounts of municipal wastes. Nor is it realistic today to require Chicago to stop sending its sewage down the Illinois River, washing it along with water drawn from Lake Michigan. Great improvements are possible. But no real alternatives have yet come from the drawing boards to match Chicago's more than 3,500,000 people and the industries that support them. Washington, D.C., has no known choice but to continue using the Potomac River to carry off its wastes.

This role of water is now accepted into Federal law regarding the plans for all new reservoirs. A part of the water taken into a reservoir from a river must be earmarked for "low flow augmentation," to dilute and flush away wastes in the river itself during any period of drought. Each call for release from the reservoirs comes at those very times when they too are already considerably depleted, and the cities that depend upon them for municipal water seem endangered. It was on this basis that Joseph V. B. Wells, the rivermaster appointed under the system established by the United States Supreme Court, specified from day to day the amounts to be released from New York City's reservoirs into the Delaware River during the drought of 1963: 335 million gallons on October 16, and 332 million on the 17th. This water came originally from tributaries of the Delaware, from the Neversink River into the Neversink Reservoir, and from the East Branch River into the Pepacton Reservoir. Already these impoundments were down to 2.0 and 8.1 percent of capacity. Yet the release was made and the Delaware continued to carry its load of sewage. On the same dates, New York City withdrew 350 million and 240 million gallons from the same reservoirs despite a temporarily intensified drive to save water and repair leaks in the system.

These dilemmas on a national scale sometimes lead to a sense of smug security among the residents of both the newest suburbs and the oldest villages. When these people hear of the polluted water others have to drink, they feel secure in their own deep wells and efficient septic tanks, each remote from the other in lots of generous size. Twenty-three million people in the United States are estimated to rely upon this private form of waste disposal. But many of the installations fail in one or the other of the minimum requirements now set by conscientious engineers. For a three-bedroom house, they specify a pattern of pipes from the septic tank spreading over an area of 1,000 square feet in what is known as "60-minute soil." In earth of this porosity, the waste water sinks for a full hour before reaching the underground supply from which anyone else might withdraw drinking water. In the soil it leaves behind the organic matter where bacteria can decompose it.

Inadequacies and failures of these private systems may go undetected for years. Then, as occurred recently in a Kentucky village, disease virus travels the trail from one water supply to the next and officers of the health department trace it down. In this case, hepatitis spread in a pattern that led the investigators to one home. They poured a colored dye into the drain line of the suspected house and waited. Within a short time—in one instance less than thirty hours—the dye appeared in the well water of seven different neighbors. Each of these people had felt secure, because his drinking water came from a private well reaching between 80 and 200 feet below the surface of the ground. Each, for years, had been drinking sewage without realizing it.

Even the drainage basins from which water trickles into public reservoirs for cities are no longer secure. Along the fringes and the crests of the hills, suburban families are building and installing septic tanks. No one has a right to feel entirely safe as the population grows. The best we can hope is that our elected officials are doing their work conscientiously and

alertly in our behalf. But they too are handicapped, and often too busy to forestall accidents.

Until recently our confidence was encouraged by the virtual disappearance from Anglo-America and many parts of Europe of contagious diseases carried by water. The liquid we could draw from the faucet might be unpleasant to drink "straight," or even malodorous when it steamed from a shower bath. But the scent of chlorination is one we have been trained to associate with cleanliness. "It never kills anybody," we told ourselves, even when we avoided it by drinking bottled beverages or hid the flavor with coffee or tea.

Probably this attitude could have been maintained for years more if the various detergent substitutes for soap had not been invented and adopted widely. The chief advantage in these materials is their ability to work effectively in any kind of water, hard or soft, without leaving a curd. With the aid of their chemists, manufacturers of detergents could brag about the speed with which a soaplike foam appeared. By advertising, the consumers were encouraged to believe that the higher the suds the better was the cleansing action.

Almost all of the washday products on the shelves at the supermarket now have as their base a synthetic compound that was invented to do what soap does, and do it better. All of these substances overcome the natural repulsion between water and fats, whether they are oils, greases, or even waxes. They serve as intermediaries between the molecules of fat and water, making water wetter, letting it surround each minute particle of fat and dirt that is exposed by mechanical agitation. Then the fat and dirt can be rinsed away together. Old-fashioned soap plays its role in this process because it repels water and clings to fats at each tip of its three-pronged molecules, while attracting water where the prongs join together. The chemists synthesized substitutes for soap with a multiplicity of prong tips having affinity for fats, and plenty of areas attractive to water.

Besides mild soaps used on human skin, the housewives of America now buy more than 500,000 tons of detergents every year. In Great Britain, with less than a third as many people but more dirt from greasy coal smoke, an estimated 246,000 tons of detergents were used in 1962. Away with the rinse water goes this mountain of material, into streams, lakes and septic tanks. So little of its foaming power has been lost that New York City currently spends more than a million dollars a year merely to reduce the froth on its sewage at the treatment plants. Otherwise it accumulates to a thickness of many feet and is blown by the wind, to the extreme annoyance of everyone living in the vicinity.

According to senior Senator Robert S. Kerr of Oklahoma in 1961, about 30,000 sewage outlets empty into the streams, rivers, and lakes of the United States. All but 10,500 of these come from municipalities which provide no treatment whatever for the wastes. Fortunately, the 10,500 includes many of the large cities, leaving only a fourth of the nation's sewage to be dumped raw. Out of 120 million people with sewer systems, 76 million pay for some tidying up after themselves. But even this praise must be qualified, since 31 percent of the sewage gets only what is known as "primary treatment." From it, sticks, rags, paper and heavy objects are removed— things that gravity can cause to float or to sink to the bottom. At best this gets rid of only about a third of the wastes of animal or vegetable origin, and essentially none of the detergents. Often the separation process is hurried, preventing full gain from the principle Mark Twain remarked upon: "If you let water stand long enough, you can separate the land from the water as easy as Genesis."

The new detergents foamed over the complacency of people who had their own deep wells and septic tanks, and humbled those who prided themselves on having paid for municipal treatment plants for drinking water and complete purification of sewage. This secondary purification relies upon the activity of bacteria, which can remove up to nine-tenths of the organic matter. When operated under ideal conditions and followed by thorough filtration, the process releases for discharge into flowing water or ground waters only a bacteria-free liquid long regarded as being fit to drink. Even the best sewage treatment, however, does not remove inorganic materials from solution. Nor, it was discovered, can the bacteria cope with the new detergents, the molecules of which correspond to few of the digestive agents in the repertoire of the decay organisms.

Without the benefits of rapid decay, which has become known as "biodegradation," the detergents tend to remain unchanged and to accumulate. The artificial substitutes for soap pass through the sewage treatment plants and also seep through the soil into underground reserves from which users of wells draw their drinking water. People become alarmed when the glassful of water they draw from the faucet wears a head of foam as much as two inches high—a foam that does not collapse for many minutes.

So far, no illness has been shown to come from drinking water that is contaminated with detergents. Only the construction engineers have complained that gravel and sand soaked with such water makes unreliable concrete. But so annoying has the foam become that legislators are introducing measures to outlaw the sale of any detergent that is not destroyed readily by the natural processes of decay. West Germany has led the world in clamping down, by prohibiting after the beginning of October, 1964, the use of any detergents that are less than 80 percent biodegradable. Chemical engineers are trying desperately to find ways to alter the detergent molecules until bacteria will act on them quickly, without losing the features that encourage housewives to prefer the commercial products to soap.

One element of wry humor can be seen in all of this scurrying for degradable detergents. The foaming quality, which housewives have been taught to regard as essential and which makes contamination so evident in supplies of fresh water, actually is unimportant in the cleansing action. Nonfoaming detergents are just as easy to make. But now they are almost impossible to sell. If people had not been led to equate a rich lather with cleaning action, the makers of detergents would have saved millions of dollars spent on putting "foam boosters" into their products. The presence of undegraded synthetic compounds in drinking water, as in sewage, might have gone undetected for many years to come. A deliberate attempt to increase sales by misleading the consumer has backfired and struck the detergent makers exactly at the time when potential poisons in our environment are frightening people on all sides.

Biodegradation has a new sound. Yet it is as old as life itself. Only by the death and dissolution of plants, animals, and people can new life arise from the truly limited quantity of each chemical element on earth. We may prefer to forget the essential roles played by the decay bacteria in this intricate cycling of raw materials. We can overlook the extent to which a Britisher is beef and potatoes, wheat bread and tea. But when we come to count our atoms, it should be clear that each of us harbors some of the selfsame carbon and calcium, iron and oxygen as once constituted the dinosaurs of the Age of Reptiles; and before that the giant swamp plants or the first insects in the Coal Ages; and still earlier some of the strange fishes that swam in Devonian seas. If it were not for decay, the organic compounds in particular would accumulate until all life ended in starvation. The only facets that are new in biodegradation are the amounts and kinds of materials to be destroyed. Sewage plants may collect more to be decomposed than the decomposers can handle. And modern detergents are still hard for them to digest.

Even the replacement of indigestible detergents with degradable ones on the shelves of the supermarkets will not quickly rid the civilized world of the detergent foam now on its fresh waters. Yet the citizens clamor for action, feeling that somehow they must recall the sorcerer whose apprentice has produced this mess. The biologists who have been consulted see hope in culturing those decay bacteria that can best attack detergents, and in finding ways to make their action more effective. Enlistment of aid from microorganisms seems likely to prove cheapest in the long run. Chemists, however, prefer a short cut, using chemical to fight chemical.

Scientific sleuths are finding ways around the overwhelming suds. Getting the detergents out of most of the water is proving possible on a small scale. If contaminated supplies or sewage on its way to disposal is held in a tank from the bottom of which countless fine air bubbles rise, the detergent is carried into the froth and can be cleared away. The water that remains is almost free of these substitutes for soap. Engineers are trying to make this process automatic and apply it to huge volumes of solution. They are then left with a mountain of suds that somehow must be destroyed.

The chemists devised a suds destroyer containing silicones, and called it "antifoam." But it was expensive and had the disadvantage of being itself resistant to the natural processes of decay. However, tests with it led to a new discovery: the mild liquid detergents used in disinfectants, mouthwashes, shampoos, and cleaners for swimming pools have one type of molecules, whereas the alkaline flakes and powders used in dishwashers and washing machines have an opposite character. If the two types of foam are combined in correct proportions, the one neutralizes the other and the particles produced can be mordanted out of the water by adding alum.

Professor Felix Sebba, a physical chemist at the

University of the Witwatersrand in South Africa, is looking for ways to package his "contrafoam," so that it can be sprayed on detergent suds and make them vanish. Dr. William R. Samples, a civil engineer at California Institute of Technology, is working on a system, which will be self-regulating, to neutralize the detergents and eliminate them from the vast sewage outflow of Los Angeles.

So great has been the outcry over foam from detergents that other wastes in public water supplies are being overlooked. Some of them are far more dangerous to man, and all are on the increase. Most, but not all, of the difficulties can be blamed equally on the explosive growth of human populations and on the concentration of people into compact communities. In the United States, this has meant a doubling of the number of citizens, a migration of half of them into cities which spread over only 1.5 percent of the land, and a ninefold increase in industrial activities that require water and produce wastes—all in the last fifty years. In New Jersey, Rhode Island, and California, less than 14 percent of the people live in rural areas where they have space to spare.

In a sense, we are now faced with a crisis that originated early in the nineteenth century, when the growth of cities here and in Europe led to a major change in procedure. With the mass movement of people away from the farms and into the cities, to work in the factories and offices spawned by the Industrial Revolution, it seemed no longer possible to haul human wastes by cart to the outskirts of town and spread them on the soil in the sun. Instead, the storm sewers, which previously had served almost exclusively for carrying away rain and meltwater from the roofs and cobbled streets of the cities, were enlarged and transformed into underground rivers of waste. For the first time really large amounts of putrescent matter were introduced into the nearest stream or river or lake.

Dignified by the title "the water-carriage system of sewerage," this was an example of unplanned expediency. Today it might be called a "crash program." Since its inception, the same lack of rules and perspective has governed most expansion of the system of pipelines. In any year, the elected officials generally allocated the tax money they collected according to the old adage that "The wheel that does the creaking is the one that gets the grease." If a certain amount of raw sewage had to be disposed of, the taxes went farthest if the material could be dumped unobtrusively, where its concentration would not become obnoxious—at least until a new set of officials must deal with the complaints. If another community downstream had to use the same water for municipal purposes, its officials could spend taxes on filtering out the dangerous indicators of pollution, and for treating the filtrate chemically until it could cause no epidemics of disease. This was easier than to get the people upstream to clean up their waste water before emptying it into the flowing supply.

A program calling for moderation is no longer possible. Yet a system that breaks down under each recurrent strain is little better than no system. This is the basis for the report that "depletion of oxygen in river from sewage outfall killed 23,000 fish. The discharge of this sewage plant has created a problem here for some years during the canning season (August and September)." The natural agents of decay need oxygen to fulfill their role efficiently. So long as they are not overwhelmed with decomposible matter, they survive. But while working with a real abundance of organic wastes they compete with fish for the oxygen in the water, and the fish lose out.

If the sewage is excessive, the efficient oxygen users are replaced by opportunistic bacteria that thrive without oxygen. Then the people who count dead fish record: "Waste from tankage manufacturing company killed an estimated 10,000. Complete kill of all aerobic organisms. The affected portion of the stream had no discernible dissolved oxygen content for one week." Or a change in a stream may emphasize what man is doing: "Natural closure of sandbar at river mouth caused standing water receiving sewage to turn septic. Estimated number killed: 10 tons of shellfish, 5 tons of fish from 1″ to 18″ in length. Complete populations of clams, fish, mullet, flounders, crustaceans, crawdads killed."

Today the rivers of the United States contain more than six times as much pollution as they did in 1900, whereas the population has grown in these years by less than two and a half times. Many cities are now using water for domestic purposes from sources that contain twice as much pollutant as was considered safe in 1955. More than a third of the population in cities drink water that has been used before so recently that public health officials are beginning to worry. In 1962, Surgeon General Luther Terry, head of the U. S. Public Health Service, admitted: "We are by no means sure that at least some viruses are not slipping through our present water purification and disinfectant processes and entering our water mains." An official publication of his office states that "Along the Ohio River during certain times of the year, water is used nearly four times as it passes from Pittsburgh to Cairo." Some smaller cities get only the treated solution that has already been through the sewers of ten previous communities.

One of us can recall the definite change in the odor of drinking water in Toronto, Canada, whenever a south wind hurried the waters of Lake Ontario for thirty miles across the international boundary from the mouth of the Niagara River, into which Buffalo, New York, emptied its sewage. The extra chlorine was added "just in case." Years later, we learned that Rochester, New York, was equally affected by every wind from the northwest—the prevailing direction— causing Toronto's sewage to zag back across the mid- lake boundary to the place where the people of Rochester withdrew their drinking water. The thir- teenth-ranking fresh-water lake in the whole world was not big enough for dilution to hide pollution.

Now something new has been added: ships from all over the world traverse the Great Lakes after passing through the St. Lawrence Seaway. Few ships and al- most no smaller boats have any facilities for treating sewage. They dump it raw, whether into the ocean, the lake, or a harbor. They discharge it into water that soon is taken into the treatment plants that lead to municipal mains. If Surgeon General Terry is right in his suspicions that viruses can slip through, we have special reason to feel concern. These infinitesimal agents that cause disease are not the same all over the world. We may have our own immunity to those we get from residual pollution in home waters, in the low concentration that penetrates the treatment plants. We may not have the resistance required to fend off viruses from other parts of the planet, if these are introduced into our drinking water.

The water mains of today are a sanitary counterpart to the open aqueducts that brought water to the cities of two thousand and more years ago. Our sewerage system, based on water carriage, is less than two centuries old. The same water is used in both, and in one sequence the plan has great appeal. Industrial civilization is built upon water that flows from mains to sewers. It can totter if the other part of the cycle is hurried. Time is the goal—time for the water to be purified by natural means before we must use it again. Whatever the price, pure water is worth it.

DEAD WATER

AMERICA's famous pioneer Daniel Boone had a whole wilderness to explore and new rivers to discover. Neither he nor anyone else in his time would have understood the message that America's farmer-novelist, Louis Bromfield, believed so urgent: take care of the land, so that the land will take care of the people. Although the spirit of Daniel Boone still lives, we can comprehend the ideas of Bromfield better than those of the pioneers. That America's resources are limited never occurred to them.

In his youth and young maturity, Bromfield saw the rivers of America polluted with the first squandered wealth of the nation: its topsoil. Then, negligent farmers who allowed erosion to carry off the vital surface from their cleared and plowed fields could simply abandon their land and settle somewhere else. Whether the fishes died when the streams became loaded with mud from runoff water did not interest these men. But while Bromfield matured, still pressing his message, the new lands for homesteaders filled up. Shiftless ways ended because each farmer had either to care for his soil or go out of business. The rivers began to run clear again.

The effects of this change have been dramatic in other ways, despite the fact that farmlands in the nation are shrinking. In the last few decades, some 2,000,000 acres a year have been converted into highways and airports, watersheds for communities, wildlife refuges, national defense areas, flood-control projects, and places for people to live or work. Between 1930 and 1960, the number of farms in the country with less than 260 acres decreased from over 6,000,000 to 2,500,000, while the number of farms with over a thousand acres almost doubled. The family-size farm became the suburban garden. The land has been consolidated by big operators who can afford the equipment needed to follow Bromfield's advice. They fill the gullies and terrace the gentle slopes, plow on the contour and prevent erosion. These men see the gain in letting moisture sink into the soil on their own land. All over the country, the farms have taken on the efficient mien so long a feature of those run by Pennsylvania Dutchmen.

At the same time, the last twenty years have seen a progressive change from the happy, low-pollution stage to a new dilemma linked to efficient production. With increased use of DDT and other, more potent pesticides for control of insects, fungus diseases, and weeds, even the most knowledgeable farmers have been adding unintentionally a whole spectrum of poisonous chemicals to the streams that drain their land. The same chemicals are entering the underground reserves, rivers, and lakes from which people get water for domestic needs.

Occasionally a calamity strikes in an area that, for a different reason, has been under intense scrutiny.

One of this kind came in 1954, when Federal aid was extended to tree farmers who were plagued with spruce budworm. Because they have huge tracts of forest to protect until the crop of wood can be harvested, tree farmers have to plan their operations on a grand scale, comparable to that of a Texas rancher or a corn grower in Kansas. Often an airplane can serve them as a distribution machine for pesticides aimed at these extensive croplands more rapidly and efficiently than equipment on the ground.

Only a gain was expected when a crop duster was hired to spread DDT at the rate of half a pound to the acre over the forests on each side of the Northwest Miramichi River in New Brunswick. But when all of that year's hatch of young salmon died of DDT in the river, the Canadian Fisheries Research Board had complete statistics; they had been studying fish production in that river for several years. The fisheries men saw that of the year-old salmon 85 percent succumbed; so did 35 percent of the three-year-olds, which were about ready to go out to sea.

A judge as wise as Solomon would hesitate to attach a lien to the crop of the tree farmers, to benefit the salmon fishermen whose crop was ruined. The relative values of pulpwood and food fishes can scarcely be equated. If the consequences had been foreseen, it is doubtful that money from Federal taxes would have been used to favor one industry over the other. The real issue is whether any agency has the right to spread poison on an area without previously exploring the possible consequences from every conceivable angle.

Rarely is the episode repeated in the same region.

Yet the situation is a type of pollution that cannot be classed as an act of God, and shrugged away with the conviction that lightning never strikes twice in the same place. It *could* happen again, and might be worse next time. And sometimes the people who are hurt unintentionally have the power to strike back. A case of this kind came in the spring of 1963, when DDT and copper sulfate were distributed in rice fields near Sacramento, California. The intention was to safeguard the crop from fairy shrimps, which appear suddenly from dormant eggs and eat the tender buds. But the poisons were released from the irrigated land into the canals, killing over 100,000 fresh-water fishes there and causing anguish to thousands of anglers in that part of the state. Although the Sacramento Valley produces more rice than any other part of the country, the anglers who enjoy fishing along the canals could probably pool enough resources to buy out the rice farmers and their water rights—complete. Pollution is often stopped today because recreation has more wealth behind it than agriculture.

Synthetic substances that have been invented specifically to fit the farmers' needs are the new agents that pollute the water draining from agricultural land. Many of these materials are wonderfully inert, virtually immune to the agents of decay. One of them, containing silicone compounds, is now added to irrigation canals to seal the bottom sediments into an impervious sheet. By preventing the escape of water by seepage, it aids man in guiding moisture to his fields. The material is outstandingly effective when brought to a concentration of one part per thousand in the irrigation ditch. But when water containing even half this amount reaches a river in which fishes live, the fishes die. Apparently the silicone compound forms a plastic film over their gill membranes, sealing them off from oxygen.

As more and more of the synthetic chemicals are marketed and used, the nation's fishermen grow increasingly alarmed. As a group, they are highly influential and greatly interested in the welfare of the nation's fishes. Figures released recently by the U.S. Public Health Service show why they are concerned. Major damage by pollution to fresh-water fishes was found in the streams, rivers, and lakes of all states except five: Alaska, Delaware, Nevada, Oklahoma, and Vermont. The statistics point to industrial wastes as polluting twice as many bodies of water as do agricultural chemicals. But pesticides from farmlands in 1961, which was a normal year, killed an estimated 5,600,000 fishes in contrast to industry's 2,900,000. Even when the eleven largest kills are discounted as accidents, the remaining devastation averaged more than twice as great as in the previous year. Progressively the toll is rising, as greater efficiency is sought in raising crops of high quality on a minimum of land.

The fishes and fishermen gain no comfort from the fact that the discharge of pesticides into streams is unintentional. The fishes are killed just as efficiently as though someone had planned to exterminate them. Nor does expenditure of money, whether from private funds or fines or taxes, promptly restock the waters with what anglers want. Until the insects and other types of food the fishes eat have re-established themselves—a process in which man rarely helps—the stream or lake has become "dead water," offering a livelihood only to the agents of decay.

In the laboratories of the U. S. Public Health Service in Cincinnati, a research team headed by Dr. C. H. Tarzwell has been discovering many unsuspected facets in the pollution of inland waters. At first, virtually everyone was astonished to learn that the standards of pure water established for people are far too tolerant for the good of fishes. The amount of poison that a man gets in drinking water, or through his skin while bathing, is far less in proportion to body weight than that entering a fish which uses the water as a continual environment. Most fishes in fresh water die if subjected to the amount of various chemicals that is permitted in domestic supplies.

The Cincinnati laboratory now uses living creatures to test the actual toxicity of chemicals found polluting rivers and ponds. The men try to learn what concentration of each substance will be fatal to half of the fishes in a tank within four days. The only magic in so brief a test is that time is expensive. Living bodies of wild creatures go on accumulating organic compounds, including pesticides. By the end of a month, they may build up in their bodies a correspondingly lethal concentration from a solution containing only a twentieth as much as is needed to kill 50 percent in 4 days. For this reason, the maximum to be allowed is chosen at a concentration far below the 50-percent, 4-day level.

Over the short duration of the tests, temperature is often important. DDT, for example, is absorbed more rapidly at 60 degrees Fahrenheit than at higher or lower temperatures. Given time, however, it enters anyway and becomes more toxic the longer the fishes are exposed to it. Today, virtually no fishes in fresh waters of North America within ten miles of a farm or a managed woodland are free of DDT. Some are loaded with it, and it appears to cause sterility and premature death of nestlings among fish-eating birds, such as ospreys, bald eagles, and various herons.

The insecticide endrin is the most toxic of all the chlorinated hydrocarbons, both for insects and for fish. It is fifteen times as poisonous as DDT to mammals, and thirty times as poisonous to fish. Half of the bluegill sunfish die in four days if subjected to a mere 0.5 part per billion of water. Twice this amount is required to kill some of the insects that serve as fish food. Far higher concentrations often develop in streams that receive the runoff from a field that has been sprayed to control an insect pest. Particularly is this true if the rain that causes the runoff comes within a few hours after the spraying is done.

Close behind pesticides as a modern cause of pollution are the industrial wastes added to fresh waters. Often they produce chronic problems, rather than difficulties that are acute and soon over. Recently, as noted in *The Balance of Nature*, we discovered how long a layer of sawdust lasts, preventing growth of shellfish.

At Damariscotta, Maine, the bottom of the river is still covered to a depth of from two to three feet with sawdust, although the lumbermill operators supposedly ceased dumping the material into the water half a century ago. An

equal or longer time may have to pass before the
wood fragments decompose and wash away,
leaving the bottom clean and suitable again as
a living place for clams and oysters, or as a
spawning ground for coastal fish. That the river
had a notable history before sawdust settled
there is shown by the famous heap of oyster
shells at the edge of town.

This object lesson has not sufficed in many
quarters. Along various streams in New England,
mill operators barely follow the letter of the law
enacted to protect fresh waters from pollution
with sawdust. True enough, the piles of waste
are built on dry land, where only a few crumbs
will blow into the adjacent river. But each pile
can be rebuilt annually, as it is on an area the
river will overflow in spring; flood waters regularly carry away the sawdust. The clever lumber merchant need not pay anything to dispose
of his wastes. To do so would be merely to make
money for shellfishermen or for those who
would profit from summer tourists happily enjoying an unpolluted stream.

Sometimes the actual cause of the trouble proves
elusive. One large corporation in New York State,
for example, spent a million dollars on a special device
with which to treat 6,500,000 gallons a day of waste
water. This investment was charged to public rela-
tions, following numerous complaints over dead fish
in the Buffalo River, which the wastes made poisonous. Admittedly, the distinctive and objectionable
odor of carbolic acid clung to the discharge. The new

device removed the odor, but the toxicity to fish remained unchanged. In desperation, some of the men from the Cincinnati laboratory of the Public Health Service were asked to help. On live fishes they tested samples from every fraction of waste that went into the discharge. Soon they found that one component, which totaled just 800 gallons a day, contained most of the poison. By treating this separately, the pollution problem vanished at little extra expense.

Each company is eager, of course, to get rid of wastes in the cheapest way. Usually the industry leaders are well aware of the hazards, and try to minimize them. They know that small quantities of deadly poisons, including even the cyanides, can be released into flowing rivers, so long as the water is slightly alkaline, and cause no apparent harm. Yet the situation changes spectacularly if a new industrial center is established farther upstream, and begins discharging wastes that alter the river water in the acid direction. The acid itself may have no obvious effect; fish and the living things they eat may continue to thrive in the slightly acid water. But when the ordinary amount of cyanide is added to the acidified water, its toxicity leaps upward a thousandfold. It can block the respiration of almost everything living in the river for miles below, and bring an avalanche of complaints upon the company which made no change in its mode of operation.

Usually it is easier to induce an industrial organization to clean up its wastes than to get people to do as well with their sewage outfall. Federal aid is available under the Water Pollution Control Act of 1956 to communities that are willing to tax themselves for construction of treatment centers to handle sewage and industrial wastes. But pollution increases faster than action to control or correct it. Just to keep up with the growth of population and the known increase in outfall of wastes from industry in 1962 would have required about $600 million. About $350 million actually was spent for this purpose, making it an average year.

Recently, while discussing the need for clean water with a number of young people, we heard a suggestion with much appeal: "The law provides a fine for each offense if a person discards trash along the highway," the young man began. "Why can't a law provide a similar, but stiffer, penalty for discarding refuse into a stream or river? It could be a graded scale. It might merely pay the cost of periodic inspection if the person, community, or corporation dumped only wastes that had been rendered harmless. The fine could increase progressively until it became prohibitive for release of any material that produced objectionable odor, or killed wildlife, or contained substances that decreased the usability of the water downstream." But it would be a brave legislator who would risk his future in politics by promoting such a scheme. Enforcement of a strict law would require tax dollars from more than half the people in the country, and great expense from many corporations.

Where many people are engaged in a wide variety of different types of work in a limited area, the likelihood of unforeseen pollution rises. No two mishaps may be alike, although ignorance of effect and carelessness lie behind most of them. The report from the state agency may be brief and clear—and omit mention of effects on drinking water: "Refrigerant from an overturned meat truck entered the lake and killed 3,600 fish. It affected 3 acres of the lake and lasted 7 days." "A kill of 50,000 fish resulted from drawdown of sludge digester. Digesters were emptied to make repairs to heating system." "Contractors working on one of the tunnels of the Trinity River project dumped unused concrete into Crystal Creek and allowed tunnel runoff and concrete-car wash water to enter this stream." Only one episode was necessary to eliminate the fishes. Investigation seldom goes beyond finding the immediate cause of the complaints.

Fishes are far from being the only victims. Between 8,000 and 10,000 ducks on their northward journey through Minnesota died in the spring of 1963 just after the ice broke up. Their feathers were soaked with oil. About 1,500,000 gallons of the lethal material was soybean oil from a storage tank that burst at Mankato. To this was added another million gallons of fuel oil from a broken pipe at Savage. In combination, the oils soaked the feathers of the ducks, preventing them from flying and destroying their buoyancy in the water. Noting that some of the birds sank until only their beaks were in air, the wildlife workers solemnly recorded that the oil "also affected the ducks' digestion." Conservation officials tried washing the stricken birds with detergent suds, but out of 1,000 treated in this way, only about half survived.

Perhaps these accidents, and many others that have produced equally disastrous results, could not have been foreseen and prevented. Mistakes are included in the price of progress. Possibly an end can be seen to the pollution still entering streams, lakes, and rivers from industrial centers which must use water and return it dirtier and warmer than it was before. The old problem of acid, iron, and nickel wastes from coal mines is still with us, even from shafts and tailings that have been abandoned and left un-worked for many years. Most new industrial opera-tions have a cleaner record. The engineers who plan them generally consider carefully how many tons of waste the organization will produce, and look for plant sites close to waters into which the material can be released during periods of high water without causing any distress.

Special care has gone into the locating of the few large installations and many smaller ones where compounds that are artificially radioactive have a use. "Hot" wastes are released under constant super-vision, with extra precautions taken to prevent pollu-tion from accidental spillage. Everyone realizes how essential this vigilance is, for except with a Geiger counter, or other device operated by an expert technician, these substances are undetectable until irreparable damage has been done by their radia-tions. So far, no way has been discovered to hasten the slow natural decay of radioactivity that eventu-ally makes them harmless. Instead, distance from them and dilution are the only safeguards offered.

Neither distance nor dilution is proving reliable enough to protect people from harm. The greatest care may be taken to conduct experiments in the midst of the arctic tundra, remote from any human habitation, and under conditions that protect all of the personnel working on the tests. But as soon as the outfall in waste water, or the fallout from dusts re-

leased into the atmosphere, reaches the microscopic algae that thrive in the tundra pools during an arctic summer, Pandora's box is open. The algae concentrate the radioactive compounds. So do the lichens upon which caribou feed. Waterfowl that migrate annually to these remote regions to nest rely upon the algae for food, or upon animals of small size that eat the microscopic plants. The radioactive contamination is transferred to the birds. It enters the caribou. "Hot" ducks, other waterfowl, and caribou may reveal no sign of their dangerous condition, unless they succumb to radiations from within their own bodies. The caribou migrate, and Eskimos eat them. The water birds wing southward, settling into marshes where hunters wait. The men are armed with guns, but not with Geiger counters. No ordinary person can tell whether a fine fat goose is dangerous to handle, let alone to eat.

The migrant birds discharge fecal wastes that may still contain high concentrations of radioactive material. So may the bodies of waterfowl that die of radiation sickness or of gunshot wounds too far for a hunter's dog to retrieve. Gone now is the safe distance between civilization and the remote test center in the Arctic. The radioactive compounds continue for their allotted lifetime, producing radiations in the lake of Central Park, or the city reservoirs, or the hunting ponds of West Indian islands—wherever the "hot" birds travel.

Time is essential for radioactive decay. It is indispensable for the efficient bacteria that serve all living things by keeping in circulation the atoms of decomposable molecules. Time lets the sun distill more water from the seas, and the chancy winds bring it to lands where men choose to live. Time, like fresh water and the living soil, can dilute man's wastes. But time is a resource which, like radioactivity, man cannot hurry. Time can only hurry man.

6

THE NEW RAIN GODS

HUMAN experience from countless generations is admirably distilled into the twenty-first book of the Old Testament, Ecclesiastes. But many of its sayings can be interpreted differently today than when they were set down by the unknown sage so many years ago. "Whatsoever thy hand findeth to do, do it with thy might. . . ." "He that observeth the wind shall not sow; and he that regardeth the clouds shall not reap." In those days, no one saw a way to do anything useful about the wind or the clouds. Nor had attention been focused sharply upon the need to turn man's hand in this direction, to capture moisture from the skies for human life.

Now the importance of doing something to get more water is apparent wherever the thirsts of man exceed his means to slake them. Each improvement in the standard of living for people who have been counted, and each provision for the larger populations that seem inevitable, requires fresh water. As never before, however, civilization is industrialized and dependent upon the interlocking efforts of specialists. They include sowers and reapers, and also watchers of the wind and observers of clouds. Each specialist in his own way can promote with all his might his own contribution to the common good.

A regard for the clouds and observations of the wind must have begun far back in prehistory, thousands of years before a practical use was found for them. This awareness was essential to the insight linking cause and effect in the environment, the feature that showed man to be evolving from a great ape. For the first time, this creature on the borderline realized suddenly—among other things—that the luxuriant growth in springtime depends upon previous rain that soaks the soil. It is one thing to shake the rain from one's wet fur and wait or move about mindlessly until food somehow appears. It is quite another to identify a dark cloud and first sprinkle as "April showers bring forth May flowers," and to follow by predicting the fruits of autumn.

Man progressed as he learned to modify his environment by planting cereals and vegetables, and by tending flocks of docile beasts. But no matter how carefully he prepared the soil, or chose his seed, or rotated his crops, or how well he kept his animals from overgrazing their pasture, his work came to naught if rain failed to fall. No wonder he scanned the sky so hopefully for clouds, and dreamed of incantations, offerings, and dances that might magically bring the fresh water needed by the roots.

Today man looks to his technology to fathom the rain god's secret. While the number of people who pray confidently for rain decreases toward the vanishing point, and the Rain Dance of the Hopi medicine men becomes a ritual celebration under newly-installed electric lamps, the world's storm clouds are examined with more care than ever before. By eye and with radar echoes, men plot the positions and elevations and sizes of dark clouds as viewed from the ground or from ships at sea. Aircraft fly through the lower storms and jetting rockets penetrate the higher ones to collect samples and learn the details of how invisible water vapor becomes visible mist or snow. Weather satellites monitor the earth from the outer fringes of the atmosphere. Every step in the cyclic renewal of fresh water seems open to scientific study.

The components of water do drift through interstellar space. In 1951, Harvard astronomers found free hydrogen beyond the earth's atmosphere, at a concentration of one atom per cubic centimeter; this is fewer hydrogen atoms per cubic mile of space than there are in a drop of water. Astronomers at Massachusetts Institute of Technology reported in 1963 the discovery that for each ten million free atoms of hydrogen in interstellar space there is an oxygen atom linked to a single hydrogen—an OH group. They are so rare and far apart that formation of water molecules is not expected.

The highest signs of actual water come from noctilucent ("night luminous") clouds about fifty miles above the earth. Long after the sun has set upon misty masses within reach of manned aircraft, it glints back from this great altitude into the gathering night below. Samples collected in special devices within the nose cones of rockets show that each noctilucent cloud consists of an unusually dusty region of the stratosphere. Among the dust particles, about one in five is coated with a thin film of ice crystals, making it more reflective. Presumably the water vapor rises

to this level from the earth, carried by the same air currents as shape the lofty clouds into great waves fifteen miles from crest to crest. But the dust particles themselves are suspected of being from interplanetary sources. They range from two to twenty millionths of an inch in diameter; many are larger than anything a terrestrial wind is credited with carrying so high. Moreover, the particles seem to be composed of nickel, which is a substance that is scarce in the earth's crust but common in meteoric dust. Beyond the noctilucent clouds in any direction, the particles are much rarer and none of them appears to wear a thin coat of ice.

Water vapor often condenses out as ice crystals at elevations between four and five miles above sea level, forming high cirrus clouds, which resemble thin white feathers hung in the sky. They produce no distinct shadow on earth, as clouds lower down usually do. In a cirrus cloud the individual ice crystals are so small that they ride like a froth atop the turbulent lower half of the atmosphere. Pilots of jet aircraft take their pressurized planes through the cirrus clouds to reach thinner air with unlimited visibility and almost no turbulence. They cruise in the lowest part of the stratosphere, until it is time to descend again to the next airport.

While passing through the cirrus clouds, the jet pilots have no need to fear that ice will form on the aircraft, adding dangerous weight. Although the temperature at this elevation is far below freezing, the amount of water vapor is too small to fear, and the ice crystals that comprise the clouds are well separated, suggesting a faint white dust at close range.

Most of the water in the atmosphere is carried in the lowest two miles, where some of it becomes visible as dense clouds of liquid droplets forming a foglike mist. So long as the air is relatively calm, the droplets remain separate from one another, each about 1/2500 inch in diameter. With little or no vertical movement inside such a cloud, it feels wet to the unprotected face, but sends no more than a fine drizzle to the ground below. The weather man calls it a stratus cloud, and everyone sees that it forms a dull gray blanket across the sky.

Real rain comes from still blacker clouds, which may be stratonimbus—covering the sky on a rainy day—or the "thunderheads" of summer, to which meteorologists give the name cumulonimbus because they form in the same way as the puffy cumulus clouds do, each atop an isolated rising current of air.

The rain forms when the turbulent air in the cloud pushes the fine mist droplets together mechanically, despite their repelling electrical charges. Two droplets fuse into a larger one, and to this is added another and another. Under the urging of the gusts within the cloud, the larger drops move more slowly than the smaller droplets, making collisions still more probable. Eventually the drops reach a diameter of 1/125 inch, a size at which they begin to sink through the air mass as fine rain. Under some conditions the raindrops grow still more and fall faster, eventually pelting to the ground or sea below. Under other conditions they fall into warmer, drier air beneath the cloud and evaporate completely.

Visitors to tropic seas come to expect a cumulus cloud to form above each island by mid-morning.

Often it transforms to the cumulonimbus type and cools the bit of land with a hard shower by mid-afternoon. Afterward, the cloud is a cumulus one again, seemingly tethered still above the island by an invisible cord which snaps at sunset. Then the cloud drifts away and vanishes. So regular are these events that airlines try to schedule plane service for early morning or sunset hours, when the sky will be clear and the landing fields dry. While a cumulus or cumulonimbus cloud hangs above the island, turbulent air can be predicted, and rough landings, with accidents are likely.

These changes give evidence that the morning sun routinely warms the land faster than the sea around it, and starts an upward movement of heated, lighter air. To take its place, moisture-laden breezes blow onshore from all sides. This air, in turn, is heated and rises. Soon it reaches cooler elevations where the atmospheric pressure is less, and mist forms. The cloud of condensed droplets may have its base only a mile above sea level, but by afternoon the rising column may project into the stratosphere as a great pillar as much as 75,000 feet high. Usually the stratospheric winds cut away the top of the pillar, keeping it flat there or even anvil-shaped.

At the same time of day as the moisture load above the island attains its maximum and the mass grows blackish because sunshine can no longer penetrate it, turbulence begins dashing the droplets together. Down comes the rain. But as the sun approaches the horizon, its heating effect diminishes and the great upward convection of warm moist air slows to a halt. No new additions are made to the cumulus cloud and the pillar is pushed away from the island by horizontal movements of stratospheric air. Soon its mists evaporate and the stars appear in a cloudless sky.

The considerate pilot of an aircraft does his best to guide his plane around each giant cumulus cloud if he cannot rise above it. This keeps him out of the roughest air. Often, however, he must penetrate the horizontal blankets of stratonimbus cloud and watch with utmost care the temperature outside where wings and propeller penetrate the blinding fog. Many a stratonimbus cloud is supercooled—several degrees below the freezing point, but still composed of unfrozen water droplets. With incredible speed these can congeal on the surfaces of an airplane, loading it so heavily with ice that it cannot fly. The leading edges of the wings and tail, like the air-cutting edge of each blade in the whirling propellers, dash the droplets together and ice up most rapidly. De-icing devices are now common accessories for aircraft that must be flown through supercooled stratonimbus clouds. They usually permit man to travel where he wishes despite the complexity of the great cycles of water into and out of the atmosphere.

These supercooled clouds, whether stratus or stratonimbus, are one step along toward the formation of rain or snow. But, without a nudge, they may dissipate and yield no precipitation. Even if some of the droplets freeze, becoming minute ice crystals and releasing a little heat, nothing further may happen. Before an ice crystal can serve as the nucleus for a snowflake, it has to reach a critical size.

Once this size is reached, the magic begins. Each nucleus of a flake becomes the center of a microcosm with its own microclimate, its own temperature and concentration of water vapor in the midst of the general cloud. Simultaneously the nearest water droplets in the cloud evaporate—absorbing heat—while the water vapor that is produced congeals on the central nucleus—releasing heat. Twelve molecules take their places almost simultaneously, and then another twelve, and another. Each group is oriented within the microcosm by electrical charges in the growing snowflake and by their own microscopic electromagnetic fields. So uniform are these conditions on an infinitesimal scale that each molecule appears to regulate its place in the total pattern as though directed according to what was happening on each side of all the other branches of the flake. Six rows grow in double-sided perfection. Yet no two snowflakes are ever identical.

Far more snowflakes form than fall to earth. Many of them grow heavy and drop from the parent cloud, only to sink into warm dry air which melts and vaporizes them, or into warm, moist air which transforms them into rain. If enough is known about the three-dimensional masses of air above the land, a modern meteorologist can predict with fair accuracy whether anything will happen and which form of precipitation is likely to reach the ground.

Virtually every droplet of mist in a stratonimbus or cumulonimbus cloud has at its center a microscopic particle of dust. The nucleus of each snowflake is a similar particle. Dust is not only the heart of most forms of precipitation, but also the core of man's hopes for tilting the balance in nature's weather factory in favor of more water on earth and less in clouds.

For many years, smoke particles from the burning of soft coal have been recognized as important contributors to the dense low clouds that make England so foggy. Onshore winds, from over the adjacent ocean which is warmed by the Gulf Stream, provide the moisture. Without giving up the use of soft coal, which would have meant economic disaster, the British saw no way even to cut a hole through a low cloud until the battle for Britain began in World War II. Then FIDO was invented. It had to be, to allow dispatch and landing of military aircraft regardless of fog. FIDO (for Fog, Intense, Dissipating Operation) consists of long lines of burners paralleling the airfields. The heat from inconspicuous gasoline flames in the burners warms the air enough to make it vaporize the fog. It lets the airfield be active for half an hour or so, until inward movement of more fog-bearing air replaces the heated, cleared zone between the lines of burners.

As so often happens, a less expensive way to accomplish the same thing was invented soon after the most urgent need had passed. The discovery came in July, 1946, in the research laboratories of the General Electric Corporation, where Mr. Vincent Schaefer, Jr., was trying to make rain or snow. He had a refrigerator box, rather like the open cold bins that have become standard in supermarkets to offer frozen foods. Schaefer's box had no top, and was lined with black velvet, brilliantly illuminated. He leaned over it and breathed down into the chilled air to produce a little cloud. Then into the cloud he sprinkled dust of various kinds: coal dust, fine quartz sand, sulfur crystals, and so on. All were in vain. Perhaps the air and the cloud were not cold enough.

To chill them more, Schaefer dropped over his captive cloud a handful of fine-crushed "dry ice" (crystalline carbon dioside, at a temperature of 70 degrees Fahrenheit below zero—or lower). Instantly, he saw a miniature snowstorm. Real snowflakes floated to the black velvet on the box bottom, among the particles of dry ice that had not yet vaporized.

In the same month, in the same laboratory, a colleague—Dr. Bernard Vonnegut—found another nucleus about which cloud droplets would condense. The new discovery was crystals of silver iodide, each of them a yellow prism composed of many molecules, every one a silver atom bonded to an iodine. Although each molecule of silver iodide is nearly sixteen times as heavy as a water molecule, the shape of a crystal and the disposition of its electrical charges are fortuitously similar. If crystals of silver iodide are produced in a size comparable to that of the natural ice crystals that serve as the nucleus of a snowflake, a man-made means is available for starting formation of snow.

By November, 1946, both methods were being tried on a large scale. From slow-flying aircraft cruising just above stratonimbus or cumulonimbus clouds, particles of dry ice the size of a grain of rice were "seeded" into the masses of fog droplets. Before it absorbs heat and evaporates, each bit of dry ice might induce the formation of as many as a trillion ice crystals, some of them big enough to serve as nuclei for snow. Even if the precipitation turned to rain or evaporated before reaching the ground, a long, broad path could be cleared in the cloud, giving pilots the visibility they prefer for operation. A smokelike discharge of silver-iodide crystals often had the same effect, without any extra chilling.

In the mountainous western states, experiments with ground-mounted generators for silver-iodide "smoke" have been credited with increasing the snowfall or rainfall within thirty miles by 15 to 25 percent. It is far less expensive to operate the special generators on lofty ridges than to pay for pilots and aircraft to engage in cloud seeding. The steady wind over a mountain crest carries the silver iodide aloft, and brings it into the clouds that are forming anyway. Actual precipitation, of course, can be induced only if conditions are nearly perfect for the natural event. Alternatively, the yield from a rain cloud can be increased beyond that which would fall normally. The effect, however, is limited to a zone adjacent to the mountain. Ground-based generators seem to have no influence in an open plain.

To see yellow columns of silver-iodide dust rising from a row of generators like billowing smoke, and to watch highly-trained men intently adjusting the fireless machines between periods of studying the cloud blanket, their instruments, and their charts, is to think of the custodians as modern medicine men. Just as the old-time rain makers were beset by skeptics while they sent up burnt offerings to the rain gods or chanted prayers and incantations, so too the cloud seeders are questioned today. How do you know the rain wouldn't have fallen anyway? Can you prove that you increased the yield?

In New Mexico and Colorado, the success of the Water Resources Development Corporation headed by Dr. Irving P. Krick of Denver drew criticism for being too successful. After earning a million dollars in three years by sowing silver-iodide crystals and charging clients a fee per acre of water upon delivery, the company found itself beset by lawsuits. Cloud seeding and rain making slowed to a halt. Courts were willing to rule on a question that had never been asked before: Who owns the clouds and the water they contain? If city X and farmer Y get the precipitation they pay for, does this not rob area Z, which otherwise would have benefited by the rain, farther downwind? Although there is no way to prove whether the average 1 percent of the water passing a given point and falling in precipitation under natural conditions is the same 1 percent (or less) that the rain makers try for, the cost of insurance against malpractice claims grew prohibitive. Hotel keepers were ready to sue if rain decreased the number of patrons they expected. Even people who had traffic accidents during a rainstorm saw a convenient scapegoat in the rain makers.

No one contests the worth of a different application of cloud seeding: the artificial unloading of cumulonimbus clouds before they become real thunderheads, discharging tremendous flashes of lightning from one part to another or between cloud and earth. A summer shower that lasts twice as long as it would without interference is far to be preferred to an electrical storm that sets forests and buildings afire. Farmers who fear that their crops will be ruined by summer hailstones are interested too. If each cloud that threatens to become dangerous is treated in time, an expenditure of a few hundred dollars for some work with an airplane may save many thousands. To this extent, the oft-quoted remark about the weather is becoming out of date. There now *is* a way to do something about the weather, if complaints are backed up by judicious expenditures. An extension of these techniques may also make possible the breaking-up or turning to rain of the rainstorms that spawn tornadoes and hurricanes, saving even more property and lives at bearable expense.

Since 1953, a practical realization has been in sight for the old nursery rhyme that bids "Rain, rain, go away. / Come again another day." Under Navy auspices, a research group has been working along the coast of Georgia and Florida, blackening cumulonimbus clouds with carbon dust. Just a pound and a half of dry powder distributed from an airplane around the 8,000-foot level has seemingly caused the dissipation of clouds extending vertically from as low as 3,800 feet to over 13,000. Apparently the dust blackens the cloud enough for it to absorb more solar energy, warming the air and causing the mists to evaporate within less than half an hour. It now seems possible that a Chamber of Commerce might make good a claim of some sunshine every day in the year, or no rain before noon, or some similar publicity stunt. The newspaper owners in St. Petersburg, Florida, who have long boasted about giving away their products on any day that followed one on which the sun did not break through the clouds, might save themselves money by having a hole opened in the thick overcast if it threatened to spoil the reputation of the "Sunshine City."

Once rain or snow is on the ground, far more can be done to keep it from evaporating. As Benjamin

Franklin discovered by experiment, a black square of cloth spread on a snow surface sinks in rapidly by day whereas a white one does not. The black cloth absorbs the sunlight, melting the snow beneath it. Soot has the same effect on a smaller scale, and without the pleasure that comes from an experiment yielding a clear demonstration as an answer. But people who live in communities that are threatened by snowslides and avalanches would be far happier to look out upon a mountain slope blackened regularly with carbon dust from a low-flying airplane, than to a hanging cornice of glistening snow that could crash down upon them at any moment. The likelihood of floods and of losses through erosion caused by rushing streams on hot or rainy days in spring can also be reduced if the snow is blackened in winter, and releases meltwater every sunny day.

As we watch the new rain gods churn up their pillars of yellow smoke into the lowering clouds, or the pilots buzz low over the snowfields and release black dust in winter with the same equipment they use for spreading poisons on the land in summer, we cannot dodge a pang of regret. Surely, we tell ourselves, there must be better ways for man to treat his world. Perhaps we overrate man's power, forgetful that far more energy leaps from cloud to cloud in a lively thunderhead than bursts from the biggest thermonuclear explosion ever engineered.

With a few pounds of carbon dioxide, garnered from the fermentation of a million microscopic cells of brewer's yeast, then compressed and frozen and crushed into seed-sized bits, we nudge nature ever so little and rejoice in a shower of rain. We enjoy the same sense of accomplishment that was felt by early man when the seeds he planted before the storm sprouted and grew as though at his command. But we cannot dispatch clouds of rain as we can tank cars on a railroad track, deciding that Mississippi needs no more this year and Arizona can use another shipment.

So far we have learned the good fresh water brings and the harm to us from too much or too little. But we turn man's ingenuity toward circumventing the lasting patterns of rain and snow cut from the sky by mountain peaks and the swirl of winds around the globe. We might succeed with greater ease in matching people to the world we have. Those who are willing to see their snow stay glistening white, whatever the risks, may be best fitted to dwell between the mountain peaks. People who accept snow black with soot can have their way in a city's canyons. Farmers who need rain could raise their crops where factory workers now park their cars on pavement. White cement and black asphalt can coat a desert plain just as well as a rain-kissed field.

If left alone or given a little help, the mountain soil is soon staked down by the woody roots of trees. Without payment beyond a right to live on a steep slope, they clutch the rocks and hold the rain. Against the leveling pull of gravity they fight to rise, just as a child does when he starts to toddle. By seeing a kinship between the green of the plant world and our own red blood, we might join the league of the trees. They are taller than we, and can live to greater age. Yet in reaching toward the clouds for moisture, they are on our side.

7

EACH MISTY, MOISTY MORNING

At one side of Queen's Park Savannah, the great commons in the center of Port-of-Spain on the island of Trinidad, stands a giant tree whose dense shade at midday is over a hundred feet across in any direction. No glint of sun penetrates its tiers of foliage. Yet right up to the foot of its sturdy bole, the grass grows—even more luxuriantly than beyond the shadow in the tropical sunlight. The local people call it a "rain tree," and tell visitors that at night it drips from every leaf, watering the lawn below.

Expecting to disprove this fanciful bit of local lore, we visited the rain tree just before midnight. Drops were falling. The grass below it was drenched. And from under the tree we could see straight up through its foliage to the brilliant stars—between wiping "rain" out of our eyes. A rain tree folds its leaves at nightfall, much as a clover does. Indeed, *Samanea saman*, the rain tree of the American tropics, is a member of the same family of plants; it produces pods like those of a mimosa, an acacia, a locust, or a bean. In Hawaii, to which it has been introduced, it is known as the monkey-pod tree. But so far, wherever we have met the rain tree, we have not dis-

covered how much of the tasteless liquid that drips from its closed foliage is pure dew and how much is a clear secretion from the leaves themselves.

Even by day, if the sky darkens, the leaves of a rain tree close partially. Light from the clouds in the overcast begins to penetrate, just as the starshine does at night. And if rain should fall, as it does to a total of seventy inches in an average year, much of the water promptly reaches the soil under the tremendous spreading limbs. In consequence, the precipitation on the shaded lawn may exceed that in the open. Evaporation is certainly less, because the sun is kept away.

To Trinidad, just 10.5 degrees above the Equator, the trade winds bring warm, moist air and a respectable amount of rain even during the drier months from New Year's to the end of May. Unless warmed by the heat of each sunny day, which increases the amount of moisture the atmosphere can carry, the air is close to saturation. Soon after sunset, the air does become saturated wherever it lies close to a surface that is cooling rapidly by radiating heat energy into outer space. Upon further chilling, the air begins to give up its water. The invisible vapor distills on the cool surface a molecule at a time. It clouds over each shiny object with a faint mist. Then the droplets may join into a water film of crystal purity. From slanting surfaces, such as the chromed bumpers of an automobile in the open or the folded leaflets of a rain tree, dew begins to drip.

More than a century ago, the distinguished German naturalist and statesman Alexander von Humboldt felt satisfied that he had accounted fully for the same paradoxical precipitation. "In the South American forest," he wrote, "notwithstanding the sky is perfectly clear overhead, rain frequently falls in heavy showers, caused by the copious formation of dew by the radiating powers of the tops of the trees in contact with the vapor-laden atmosphere of the Tropics."

We wish we could be so certain that this is all that goes on in a rain tree. A clear night that cools off after a hot, humid day is just the time when a great many kinds of plants are known to exude drops of clear sap from the ends of veins in their leaves. These are the jewels of jewelweed. They pearl the tips of the teeth around the edge of a grape leaf at dawn. Somewhere within the living cells, the necessary pressure is generated. Into air that is too saturated with water vapor to accept more, the plant thrusts out in droplets the residue of liquid that was absorbed at the roots, and transported up the stem or trunk. It is as though the plant had no alternative but to raise more water during the night, and then could not get rid of it except by producing an imitation dew. Sometimes the water falls rainlike to the ground.

On nights when no dew forms, some of these plants still exude their droplets at the end of veins. By touching the tongue to these glistening spheres, we have sampled them and found a faint taste of salt. But so fleeting is the flavor that it vanishes with any dilution, such as when the exudate is mixed with dew. Perhaps on some occasions the rain trees shed these tearlike drops, and cycle to the earth some of the mineral matter that their spreading roots withdraw along with moisture. Try as we might in Trinidad, we could not discern in the light of our flashlamp whether the moisture was coming from the flat surfaces of the folded leaflets (as von Humboldt would imply) or at the ends of the tiny veins. Everything within reach was wet—the leaves, the flashlight, the grass, the soil, our clothes, and the night air that wafted past our faces.

Distinguishing between water exuded by a leaf and that which has condensed on it from the air is much harder to do than distinguishing between moisture of these origins and actual rain. Falling from a cloud, or even from the foliage of a rain tree, the water drops reach the grass with a velocity and momentum great enough to carry them onward, streaking down the blades toward the soil. By contrast, a dewdrop may stay where it distilled, speared through by the tip of its cool grass blade or hanging like a jewel from a looping spider web. The exuded spheres of water tend to remain where they form from the leaves. They and the real dew are suspended well above the ground. They wet the shoes and shanks of a walker in the dawn far more thoroughly than any remains of a nighttime shower.

Those who stay indoors until after the morning sun has dried the grass seldom realize how much moisture appears from nowhere on a clear night. Many of the nocturnal animals and early birds satisfy their thirst entirely by sipping one drop after another, then waiting until the next morning to refresh themselves again. We have watched red squirrels and song sparrows take a bath in the water held by the grass blades, shoving their bodies along the ground as though swimming, until they were soaking wet.

Perhaps that close observer of the immediate scene, Gilbert White, parson of Selborne in 1776, had in mind something similar when he referred to the "swimming vapours" that drench the surfaces of things on "elevated downs." The English word *downs* for a treeless *up*land always tends to confuse us in America. As White wrote in the same February letter to his correspondent, the honorable Daines Barrington, "the air, when loaded with fogs and vapours, and even with copious dews, can alone advance a considerable and never-failing resource." This, to him, accounted completely for the little round ponds so often found at the tops of the grass-covered downs near the English coast. Despite "evaporation from sun and wind, and perpetual consumption by cattle," they "constantly maintain a moderate share of water, without overflowing in the wettest seasons, as they would do if supplied by springs." It was to a reliable pond of this sort, presumably, that the old nursery rhyme sent Jack and Jill, "up the hill" to get a pail of water. But it took a three-year program of research, sponsored by the Royal Geographical Society, to establish in 1914 that nightly fogs and mists, rather than dew, sustained the supply of fresh water.

In the cloud forests that cap many of the mountain tops in Central America, Gilbert White would have seen how right he was in noting that "in heavy fogs, on elevated situations especially, trees are perfect alembics: and no one that has not attended to such matters can imagine how much water one tree will distil in a night's time by condensing the vapour, which trickles down the twigs and boughs, so as to make the ground below quite in a float." Small, but constant, streams spill down the steep slopes of old volcanoes in the Tropics of the New World wherever these cloud forests remain uncut. But once the trees are felled to make space for crops of food, the clouds drift past and leave behind little of the moisture.

In the coastal mountains of California, the giant redwood trees fulfill a corresponding role. Winds from the west bring humid air up the slopes, where it chills by expanding at higher elevations and condenses to form mist. A grassy crest captures too little of the moisture to stay green in summer. But a redwood tree filters the fog through its glossy needles, distills extra dew, and drips so much water to the shaded ground below that ferns and other plants of humid regions thrive and spread. On the floor of a redwood grove, a rain gauge may capture from forty to seventy inches of precipitation in a year, whereas in the same site after the forest is cleared away it might record only fifteen to twenty-five. On the bared slope, a redwood seedling would soon die, but in the moist soil under tall redwoods, the young trees rise regularly, maintaining the fog forest. That some of the living, reproducing trees exceed three thousand years in age gives no real hint to the number of millennia these slopes have been clad in redwoods. Thirty generations of such patriarchs go back to man's beginnings, whereas ninety generations of men have gone since these living trees were seedlings.

When we watch a logging truck ahead of our car, winding down the curving highway through the redwood groves and over the bare hills where these great trees once stood, our minds snap like toggle switches between two visions—the alternative uses man can make of these coastal, misty, moisty slopes. One is a wonderland of grassy lots. After the morning mists have gone, each lot affords a view of other grassy lots with a view. Each lot bears its house of redwood and glass, its humming air-conditioner. Each lawn is golden brown for most of the year, its sun-baked soil endangered alternately by sweeping fires and the erosive force of winter rains. Or the same slopes can be groves of moisture-catching trees, shading and staking down the earth. They dwarf the homes set inconspicuously amidst the tremendous boles, the ferns, and the rising redwood juveniles that are readying themselves to replace each aging parent. This vision is predominantly green all year, humidified and cooled silently by the working chlorophyll in the glossy needles that tap the mists and put pure water in the dark, crumbly soil. In one view we see only people and stream beds that are dry when not deluged by storm water. In the other, there are birds and squirrels, deer and gently flowing streams—and people too.

Today there are no people, no homes, no grassy slopes, no trees near Mount Ramon in the Negev Desert of Israel, midway between the Mediterranean, the Gulf of Aqaba and the Dead Sea. Yet this desolate landscape still shows the work of people who lived there a thousand years B.C. At regular intervals in straight lines are piles of small pebbles with no sand or mud between. Each day in the brilliant sun they grow burning hot; each night they chill down more quickly than the hard-packed soil. Before the stars fade again in the light of dawn, the air next to those pebbles is cooled enough to yield a little moisture. The dew trickles through the open spaces in the pile and thoroughly wets the ground beneath. Professor Ritchie Calder of Edinburgh University, an expert on water who investigated these piles of pebbles, found evidence that the ancient inhabitants of this parched land planted olive trees and figs in the isolated spots of damp soil, and transformed the desert into groves and orchards. These people had no "misty, moisty morning, when cloudy was the weather." Their land was no coastal California or foggy English downs. They had no high volcanic peaks, or onshore trade winds bringing vapor to fall as rain. Yet, by ingenuity, they made efficient use of the great daily change in temperature that is characteristic of desert air, and gained from it the moisture for life.

The old ways are not always best, but often they are thrifty. If a pile of pebbles three feet high can continue untended for three thousand years taking moisture from the air over one of the driest deserts in the world, surely modern men have the ingenuity and equipment with which to do this more efficiently. Scanning the scene in the brilliant light of day, we see no water except in mirages. Deep wells reveal none underground, and we conclude that the few scattered rains in winter cannot support life. The large deserts seem useless unless they can be irrigated. Until recently, the idea that dew could be important in arid lands had occurred to almost no one.

Along the fringes of the Negev Desert and farther north in the Holy Land, the modern Israelis are trying desperately to rehabilitate the soil and make it produce. Every resource must be put to work with utmost thrift—even dew. There Dr. S. Duvdevani, who explored the formation of dew until he became an expert on the subject, invented a way to measure the seemingly trivial amounts that are distilled in a a field or a desert under natural conditions. Dew was heaviest in the hot dry summer when rain rarely fell. But, curiously, the amount of dew that formed seemed about the same regardless of the relative humidity of the air.

Until they had tested his dew gauge and found it to work as stated, scientists elsewhere suspected that Dr. Duvdevani's measurements of dew were far too optimistic—ten times greater than seemed reasonable. Day after day they rose at dawn to photograph the pattern of moisture that had condensed on the top of the simple instrument. To their surprise they found that every night that stayed clear in summer yielded about ¼₅ inch of moisture. For a whole year of cloudless nights, as in the Israeli arid lands and all deserts, this amounts to fifteen inches of water—half as much as the average total for rainfall in the United States.

If an extra bonus of dew amounting to fifteen inches a year is available in all the dry parts of the earth, waiting for the early birds to get it, the world takes on a new look. Perhaps Dr. Calder is right in his belief that the climate makes fewer deserts than people do. Most of our arid Southwest receives between five and fifteen inches of rain each year. So do many of the lifeless deserts in the Old World. If five inches of rain could be added to fifteen inches of garnered dew, the twenty inches of water would support a healthy prairie. A little more would be enough for wheat. Fifteen inches of rain plus fifteen of dew are enough—if spread through the year—for a forest. This would account for the forests of Guir, where Hannibal got his elephants; for the wheatfields of Libya, upon which Rome depended; and for grazing lands in many parts of the world where almost nothing grows today.

To verify the idea that so much dew is waiting, the scientists began to calculate. To their surprise, they found that on a clear night about ninety-three calories of heat are available for condensing dew each minute from each square foot of surface. This is almost half of the amount of heat energy radiated into space from the cooling earth. Where the air is extra dry, less dew condenses for each calorie of heat radiated into space; but through dry air heat radiates freely, dropping the nighttime temperature many degrees and making more calories available for condensing dew. Somewhat moister air reduces the rate at which heat is radiated into the night, and the temperature changes less; but the efficiency in producing dew is higher, and the total amount formed is about the same.

The pessimist among German philosophers, Arthur Schopenhauer, might have found satisfaction in these discoveries about dew. They fit perfectly his account of progress in human knowledge. First the idea, such as getting usable water from dew, is ridiculous. Next, as when an honest dew gauge is invented, it might be worth trying. And now that we look at the piles of pebbles in the Negev Desert, and make the appropriate calculations, we reach the final stage: it's too simple to be called an invention. But the real test is still ahead. On a large scale, no one has yet constructed a device to improve on the piles of pebbles. We need an installation costing very little more, but capable of gathering in all fifteen inches of dew from every acre of arid lands, and putting it to work. As moisture for grass or as drink for people and animals, its importance may well outweigh the gain from more olive orchards or groves of figs.

Until now, civilized man has seen no great gain from taking a Lilliputian view, looking into dewdrops as though they were crystal balls and showed the future. Yet, in just those parts of the world where rain is scarcest, this pure water is ready, waiting. Earlier than the dawn and the hope of a new day comes this silent condensation, this bounty more than half forgotten. Without thinking of the words, for more than a century the people of America have sung of it around the campfire. Stephen Foster sang them first, and left us his message: "Starlight and dewdrops are waiting for thee."

8

GREEN UMBRELLAS TO HOLD THE WATER

As the first forests began overspreading the land about 335 million years ago, they changed the world. The force of the storms was tempered by leaves held on the interlacing branches of the trees. Wherever forests stood, the sun and rain could no longer beat down, alternately baking and scouring the continents. Fallen leaves and branches accumulated and slowly decomposed; under them a soil built up. Live roots, delving in the soil, reinforced it, and held it as a reliable seed bed for young trees.

Under the shade of the forest foliage, the land became hospitable to less sturdy kinds of life. Protected from the full strength of the summer sun, from the driest air, from winds, a wealth of other vegetation found a place. It grew on the soil and clung to the tree trunks. And animals got food where none had been before.

The plants, whether woody or not, are today the most stationary, reliable members of a swarming community of living things. The community, not just the trees, constitutes the forest. Insects eat the topmost leaves, and deer browse on the fresh growth near the ground. Tree frogs and birds catch the in-

sects; beetles and their young cut tunnels in the tree trunks; woodpeckers drill for the beetles. Other creatures burrow through the soil among the roots and assist the agents of decay in transforming the fallen vegetation, making its elements available once more to the trees.

In classical Greece, the forests so impressed Theophrastus of Eresus, Aristotle's famous student, that he classified the green world into "trees, shrubs, undershrubs, and herbs." Each summer shower wets the woodland anywhere in that sequence. Repeatedly the gentle rain is intercepted by the leaves in tiers. Until all are wet, from the topmost branch to the lowliest herb, less rain reaches the soil than beyond the forest fringe.

Of the water that adheres to the foliage, most evaporates again. Even the slender needles of pines, both green ones on the trees and brown ones decaying to form a resinous duff of organic matter on the forest floor, can have this effect. In the lofty Sierra Nevada of California, a stand of western yellow pine averaging eighty years in age, dissipates 88 percent of the annual precipitation in ordinary years. Only 12 percent gets through the duff and soaks into the underlying soil. In contributing to the production of three to four tons of new wood per acre each growing season, about four thousand tons of water evaporates from the trees, to the benefit of no one.

Despite this interference, forests remain the world's best traps for fresh water. Over the whole United States, three-fourths of the tree-clad land serves in a major or moderate way to capture and release in useful form the moisture upon which we all depend. Of the water that we use, fully two-thirds trickles out of hillsides and mountains that are covered by forests. So consistently do the trees in the West grow at elevations where most of the snow and rain drops from the clouds that these areas dole out more than half of the water that becomes available there, supporting life in the sunny, shadeless valleys.

Live green umbrellas still cover a third of the land in the United States, and slightly more in bordering Canada. They stabilize the soil and our supplies of fresh water so outstandingly that we scarcely realize our own good fortune. Our continent has a distinct corner on the fresh-water resources of the planet, even though South America has the largest river (the Amazon) and Africa both the second largest (the Congo) and the longest (the Nile). In North America are half of the thirty largest lakes on earth, and an incredible number of smaller ones. Most of them are in forest land, where the glaciers of the Ice Ages scoured pockets in the rock. Lake Superior is the largest fresh-water lake of all. It and the four other Great Lakes along the border between the United States and Canada contain among them more than a fourth of the fresh water held by all of the lakes and all of the rivers on earth.

With barely a twentieth of the world's land surface at our disposal, we have a unique wealth in usable moisture. At home it is taken for granted; abroad it is envied almost hopelessly. An accident of nature— and the fact that we have not yet cut all our forests— has made possible the building in the New World of a civilization based upon this abundance of fresh water. To people elsewhere, who notice the water more than they do the forests close by, it seems incredible that we are already feeling the approach of a water shortage. Yet we are striving as strenuously as anywhere on earth to fend off our growing thirst.

With a little ingenuity, it should be possible to make our green umbrellas deliver still more water to the soil, without reducing the other benefits the forest lands confer. The extra water they might produce is no more vital than their yield of our largest crop (wood), or their value in protecting us against disastrous floods and soil erosion, or their place in recreation.

One way we gain is by decreasing the number of leaves that must be coated with a film of water before rain begins reaching the soil as fast as it falls. Tree farmers work in this direction when they remove the shrubby undergrowth and the "weed trees" that have no commercial value. They spare enough seedlings of valuable kinds to replace the mature trees when these are cut. Sometimes such a simple change, attended to once every four or five years, gets enough more rain and meltwater into the soil to increase by 30 to 50 percent the flow of streams fed by woodland springs.

To discover how much thinning is worthwhile, several ideas are being tried out in North Carolina. In the most drastic treatment near the Coweeta Hydrologic Laboratory, the forestry crew cut all of the woody vegetation from a small watershed. They took care to disturb the soil as little as possible, and left the logs and cut material on the ground to decay. The following year the streams there carried 65 percent more water than had been recorded previously, and showed no decrease in quality or signs of erosion or flooding after storms. In the next year, however, the gain was less because sprouts from the surviving stumps used up so much moisture. And as the cut wood dried out, the hazard of a devastating forest fire frightened everyone within many miles.

From an adjacent watershed, foresters E. A. Johnson and J. L. Kovner carefully removed all of the dense understory of laurel and rhododendron, which averaged between ten and twenty-five feet in height. During winter these shrubby growths release into the air a surprising amount of water, because they are evergreens. When all of them were cut off as close to the ground as possible, disturbing the soil and litter only slightly, the depth of water in the drainage streams increased by an average of 2.8 inches. As the understory regenerated, this gain too declined. But at the end of the sixth year, when the streams were only 1.24 inches deeper than before the cutting was done, the average improvement during the experiment was still 2 inches. In a flowing stream, this represents a great deal of water.

Nature rarely provides less than two layers of vegetation between the earth and the open sky. In any forest, the foliage of the trees serves as the first brake on the speed of the falling drops. The duff of fallen leaves and twigs provides another. The litter on the soil is the more valuable, and the one that ordinarily remains in place. It thickens and shields the soil from autumn rains in forests of hardwoods that shed their leaves in winter.

Merely by examing the duff, a good forester can

tell how well or poorly the forest will trap the rain that falls on it. Where the forest floor is ripped up by careless logging, or trampled by grazing animals, or burned badly by a fire, the rain may run over the ground and cause erosion instead of sinking in. To renew the duff, the trees are needed overhead—as well as to produce the wood the forester wants. If duff is to shield the soil at all seasons from sunlight and rain that might strike the ground directly, the duff must be renewed as rapidly as decay simplifies it to compounds that dissolve and are leached away.

To the running water from rain or melting snow the soil of a forest has open a multitude of channels. Between 50 and 60 percent of the total volume of forest soil is space between the particles of mineral and organic matter. Some of these passageways are less than a hundredth of an inch across, and hold water by capillarity against the force of gravity. They retain in storage a surprising amount of moisture. Most of it will eventually be lost from the soil, by evaporation or by absorption into the roots of plants. Of the water they take in, nine-tenths flows upward to the leaves and there is released into the atmosphere.

Larger passageways are open in forest soil. They are used daily by earthworms and insects, or they show the locations of roots that died, decomposed, and were dissolved away. Dr. R. N. Gaiser, who counted these major passages in an acre of hardwood forest in Ohio, found an average of one to the square yard. Down these conduits, each a quarter of an inch or more in diameter, the soil water can move rapidly, propelled by gravity. Even after they are filled, the movement continues slowly as the moisture filters from one channel to another, both vertically and horizontally. It replenishes the supplies of ground water. Eventually, much of it reappears in bubbling springs that keep the rivers flowing.

We and every other living thing gain by having the soil spaces open, ready to sponge up the rain and meltwater. Only by having the liquid enter the underground reservoirs to be doled out again long after the rain has ceased or the snow disappeared can the water table be kept high and the rivers continue to flow all summer. Yet often the countless insects and worms that burrow below the trees are scorned, instead of valued for their work. Decaying roots are regarded, if at all, as utterly useless. In the long view, they are temporary plugs in future channels for rain —water that someday may be drawn clear and fresh as a glassful fit to drink.

The force of growth in live roots serves the whole living world on land when it pushes the soil aside and opens these channels of the future. Impatient, thirsty man sometimes begrudges the roots the water they absorb while doing this work. The nine-tenths of it that is dissipated into air seems a complete waste, although it has already acted as the solvent for dilute solutions of mineral substances carried upward in the plant. We easily forget that the important minerals in our food, and the production of a valuable crop of wood, depend upon this upward current of water from the soil through the conducting cells of plants. No one has invented a better or a cheaper way.

Without the duff constantly renewed upon the soil and without the roots of trees that die and leave passages for descending water, a land that once knew forest shade grows inhospitable. This essential connection between extensive groves of trees and the fresh waters on which man and many other kinds of life depend was apparent at the time of the American Revolution to the gentle British parson in Selborne. Gilbert White commented to his correspondent: "That trees are great promoters of lakes and rivers appears from a well-known fact in North America, for, since the woods and forests have been grubbed and cleared, all bodies of water are much diminished, so that some streams, that were very considerable a century ago, will not now drive a common mill."

Gilbert White may not have realized that these rivers of America still carry past the abandoned mill sites about the same total amount of water every year as they did before the forests were cleared. It simply rushes past in spring and after every spell of rainy weather, leaving so little to flow in summer as to be useless for water power. Often the level rises to flood stages, and the rivers carry off piecemeal the remains of the mills they used to drive.

Predicting and preventing floods have become important to people who live or work in the lowlands near a river. Often the change that would succeed best over the decades and centuries is to reforest many of the watersheds from which the river drains. But as the English patriot and philosopher John Evelyn remarked in 1664, "Men seldom plant trees till they begin to be wise, that is, till they grow old, and find, by experience, the prudence and the necessity of it."

To replace the duff and rebuild the soil, until it

will catch the water and delay the runoff, takes years. Yet the spongy ground that develops under a stand of trees is the best known for this role. It provides the fullest natural protection against erosive forces which can tear away the land and silt up the quiet waters. The effectiveness of the litter can often be seen when a second heavy storm follows soon after an earlier one. The first rain, perhaps breaking a span of dry weather, reaches large spaces in the soil which were fairly empty. During the initial rain, they take in all of the water. But the following storm, hard on the heels of the first, comes to storage spaces that are already almost full. Temporary rivulets stream over the surface of the woodland, as though testing the matted litter on the ground and the tangled roots below for weak places where erosion can begin.

Wherever people are endangered alternately by floods and thirst, our earth might be made hospitable again, if only a determined application were made of modern knowledge about the paths of rainwater over and through the soil. Almost certainly a wealth of water could be provided for Mexico City, if just one change made during the Spanish occupation were undone. Of the Aztec Indians they conquered the Spaniards demanded gold, slaves, food, and charcoal. The gold they hauled to Europe, where it gave Spain a temporary glitter. The slaves mostly died or escaped before reaching the coast. The food the Spaniards ate. None of these tributes cost the Aztecs enough to matter; in a generation or two the Indians could easily have rebuilt their world. Instead, ruin struck them in a simpler guise. To provide charcoal for the chilly Spaniards, they had to fell all of the hilltop forests that rimmed the lofty saucer-shaped plateau. Before new growth could rise, the summer rains carried off the hilltop soil in a tremendous flood of mud.

To Mexico City, two-thirds of the year's rain comes in four months of summer, at an average rate of five inches a month. It ruined the terraced gardens where the Aztecs raised their food. It flooded their homes and pathways by September, as the marshes and lakes around the city overflowed. It dispersed the fishes, which previously had provided the Indians with abundant protein. And then, for the next eight months, the water all but ceased to flow. The lake level fell as the streams dried up. The fishes died. Year after year these calamities continued until about 1900, when engineers cut drains through the rim of the plateau and led the summer floods away. The rains still come. But no one has yet restored the hilltop forests, which could again regulate the flow of water more reliably than all of the engineers.

In Mexico City, in Spain, in parts of North Africa, and in Greece, few people realize that once the forests stood where scarcely a tree exists today. In the twenty-eight centuries since Homer wrote his epic poems, the sounds of the forest have vanished from his native land. No longer does his description of the noise of battle bring to mind "the din of woodcutters in the glades of a mountain," for the trees and the woodcutters have long been gone. To hear this sound, a Greek must leave the country, or climb to places that are almost inaccessible.

In North Africa, where the forests are no more,

people are now discovering water deep in the soil. The Tunisians are rehabilitating wells that were dug by the Romans, some to a depth of 328 feet. At the bottom is good water that has flowed under the ruins for centuries, unused. Below the Sahara this hidden river goes, from high in the Atlas Mountains where forests still grow beyond easy reach of man. Through a thick layer of porous sandstone the water flows, to emerge from some unknown springs in the bottom of the Mediterranean Sea.

Another flowing, subterranean lake in the interstices of rock underlies the Great Sand Sea—the Giant Erg—of Western Egypt. Water from the mountain forests along the border between Chad and the Sudan travels northward parallel to the Nile for almost a thousand miles. It is believed to nourish the oases of Al Kufrah in eastern Libya and Siwah in Egypt, before slipping under the desolate Qattara Depression (whose floor is 436 feet below sea level) to reach the Mediterranean. These deserts too may once have supported forests, before people took to cutting every bit of vegetation and burning it for fuel. Many of the really lifeless areas on our planet are not natural, but man-made. They could be unmade almost as easily.

At Khartoum in the Sudan, no woodland has stood naturally for many years—perhaps not since the last days of the Ice Ages, when Africa was forested from the Indian Ocean to the Atlantic. Although the White Nile flows on one side of the city and meets the Blue Nile from the other side, the soil beyond the rivers is desert dry. With only the present rainfall of five inches a year, trees cannot grow. Yet now a national forest is rising, as a source of firewood and lumber close to the city boundary. It is a green monument to native ingenuity and thrift, for the Nile water that irrigates the growing trees reaches them only after it has carried the sewage of Khartoum to the modern treatment plant. Instead of polluting the Nile with the effluent, or letting the water evaporate uselessly into the desert air, the Sudanese engineers have put the much-used liquid to work again.

Already, under the direction of Dr. M. K. Shawki, the men of the Forests Department are proudly trimming their young trees and getting enough salable fuel to pay for part of the operations. Tree branches are knitting together into a canopy, reducing evaporative losses from the irrigation system. This permits a diversion of effluent water to new groves around the periphery. But the whole undertaking is a success only because of a protective fence and alert patrols, which keep out domestic animals and unauthorized people. Until the idea of saving the green umbrellas into a productive future can gain wide acceptance among the Sudanese—which will require time and education—the national forest must be guarded like a precious gem.

Each forest is man's ally in increasing the amount of useful life and water on the land. Yet for perhaps a million years man has been exposing the soil to the sun by killing trees. For 335 times as long the communities of trees have been building that soil and charging it with water. Fortunately, in many parts of the world, the last century has brought a new realization of the role of forests, and of man's need for the water they can conserve. Today, so much is known about the cyclic movements of the world's moisture that the opportunities we overlook seem endless.

Better than ever before, we can estimate just how much water there is. The total amount that man can ever turn to serve his ends is so small that thrift seems inescapable. Less than 3 percent of all the water in the world is fresh—on the continents or in the soil; the rest is salty. Of that less than 3 percent, almost four-fifths is locked away in polar ice caps and giant glaciers, from which icebergs break off and slowly melt at sea. Another tenth or more is in rock crevices and between mineral particles that lie deeper than half a mile below the land surface; this water is practically unavailable, because to pump it from more than 2,640 feet down is too expensive. This leaves 0.32 percent of the world's water where trees and man can reach and use it—in the atmosphere, in fresh-water lakes and streams, and in the top half-mile of soil.

Over most of the continents, between a third and a twelfth of the precipitation that the forests trap finds its way into the soil. In the United States, with an annual rainfall averaging thirty inches, the soil gains between three and ten inches of water each year. For any region with less than the average rainfall, or with too little forest land to capture the rain that comes, the amount is correspondingly less. Since between fifty and two hundred times this much water remains naturally in the top half-mile of soil and sediments, the available moisture in the ground represents the accumulation of between fifty years and two centuries. When we drill a well and draw from the store of water above the half-mile limit, we are penetrating the past. We can borrow from this liquid capital, so long as we regularly and faithfully repay each debt. It is largely the treasure of the forest trees, and we need their continued help to maintain so vital a resource. They are our green umbrellas against a future thirst.

9

WETLANDS

TRAVELERS who crisscross the continent by air, or who drive its highways, see the countless lakes in some of the glaciated northern states. They might believe that Minnesota or Maine has the most wetlands. Part of the arid Southwest surely would possess the least. But a lake is not a wetland unless its depth is 10 feet or less. A wetland is merely an area where, for part of the year at least, water stands naturally from one inch to 120 inches deep.

Today the United States still has about 118,000 square miles of wetlands, not including those of Alaska or Hawaii. They amount to 4 percent of the total area. Florida leads the list of wetland states, with 45 percent of its land under water for at least some weeks. Louisiana, with 31 percent, is second. At the end of the list comes West Virginia, with New Hampshire a close competitor. In these the land is too tilted for water to stand on it for long.

Many of the nation's northern wetlands serve in summer as a great "duck factory"; southern ones provide places for waterfowl to congregate while winter comes and goes in the nesting areas. For this reason, the U.S. Fish and Wildlife Service keeps a

detailed inventory of the resource. Of all the wetlands, 105,400 square miles are wet with fresh water.
Some hold it only in springtime and after heavy
rains. Others remain wet at all seasons, as great
sunny marshes in which muskrats are at home; or
as dense swamps, shaded by shrubs and tall trees,
such as bald cypresses.

Each wetland seems to have almost as many different characters as the people who look at it. We
see this in a New England community we know well.
It has a shallow millpond close to the residential
area. Our friends in town who hunt, long for the
edible waterfowl on the quiet backwaters of the pond,
knowing that it is illegal to discharge a gun within
the town limits. People who enjoy watching birds
murmur with delight when a mother black duck
with nine ducklings sails like a convoy from one
patch of cattails to another. Muskrats build nests in
the marshy borders, and one neighbor has done
rather well by trapping them for fur. Many of the
townsfolk admire the water lilies that bloom each
summer in the deepest areas, and the purple pickerel-
weed around the muddy margins.

They prize the reflections of the white church
steeple and of the flaming foliage of swamp maples
when autumn tints the land. But the road crew
dumps sand and gravel, rocks, and other solid fill
into the pond margins. Ten to thirty feet of new land
have been built in this way along one side of the pond
during the past five years. We think about this and
wonder how soon there will be pondside lots for sale,
houses on them, and new taxes coming to the town.
Perhaps the selectmen think about this too. Possibly

they regard taxes as the deciding factor when weighing requests from the townspeople. Some want the pond dredged so that it can be used by water skiers; others urge that the waters be drained completely so that children will not drown in the "quagmire." Probably no feature of wetlands makes them so vulnerable as the smallness of the taxes coming from them.

Our local pond is held by a concrete dam built just before World War I, when the mill at its end was still operating. Now the steel bars used as reinforcement in the concrete are being exposed by erosion, and rusting away. We judge that the whole structure will collapse in the next decade or two, and suspect that the citizens at Town Meeting the following April will be invited to decide how much they will tax themselves to rebuild it. Probably it will be cheaper to put the shrunken river in a large tube of concrete pipe, and fill the pond completely with new house lots, cross it with paved streets, and forget it ever existed. Conversions of this kind, and comparable ones that produced more farmlands, have already obliterated about 70,400 square miles of wetlands in the United States since 1849, when Congress passed the first Swamp Land Act.

We know we are being sentimental when we think of the little blue heron who came so often to stand motionless between stabs at polliwogs in a bit of marsh where a new house is going up. The owners will never hear the vocal proclamations of spring by diminutive tree frogs—the peepers—or by trilling toads, in the water where their home is to be. It is quite possible that their children, born within ear-

shot of the big millpond, will have no pond to re-
member by the time they go to school and are introduced to the sound of amphibian voices from a pho-
nograph or a tape machine. We are reactionary to
prefer these calls to the stuttering voice of a power
lawnmower, or to espouse the dank mists of morning
rising from the millpond rather than the smog of
automobile exhausts as our neighbors haul their
children to the community schools.

The drive for reclamation is a sentiment that has
been held more widely ever since the middle of the
nineteenth century, when Congress granted to
Louisiana all swamp and overflow lands then unfit
for agriculture. No area of the public domain had
visible value until it became settled—and ceased
to be public domain. Wetlands seemed menacing,
a hindrance to land development. This attitude appears to be almost unanimous among the city dwellers who visit us today. And, according to the 1960
census, there are twelve urbanites for each person
who lives in the countryside, where wetlands are
more accepted as a normal part of the landscape.

Perhaps the chief hope of maintaining a sizeable
part of the country in marsh and swamp lies with the
millions of waterfowl hunters and sport fishermen
who come from the cities. They spend almost $4
billion a year on these outdoor hobbies, on weekends
and short vacations beyond the city limits. These
people know how much it is in their interests to hold
the line somewhere on drainage and obliteration of
the nation's wetland resources. Although 80 percent
of the waterfowl breed in Canada and Alaska, the
rest chiefly in the wetlands of the north central

states, the maintenance of these bird populations depends upon the existence of suitable places in other states at the southern end of the annual migration. A great diversity of wetland sites is essential to spread the waterfowl over as many states as possible, giving hunters in each a chance to enjoy their sport.

Supervision over migratory waterfowl is maintained by the Bureau of Sport Fisheries and Wildlife, in the Department of the Interior. This department, created in 1849 by the same Congress that enacted the first Swamp Land Act, has become the country's principal conservation agency, despite conflicts of motives internally. While the bureau concerned with waterfowl and native wildlife attempts to improve the wetlands along the great flyways used by ducks and other birds, the Bureau of Reclamation in the same department often encourages the conversion of wetlands into acres on which food crops can be raised. Simultaneously in many years, agents of the Department of Agriculture try to take land out of production, to reduce the burden of unsalable farm products without jeopardizing the livelihood of farmers. Hunters of waterfowl and others have been critical of the spending of tax money on the one hand to improve conditions for wildlife and on the other to destroy suitable areas already in existence. Perhaps a clearer policy will emerge from the agreement reached in 1963 for closer cooperation between the Departments of Interior and Agriculture.

Growing importance is seen in the wetlands as storage centers for ground water, as a means for stabilizing runoff and in this way aiding in flood control, and as a reliable way to reduce erosion. Holding water on the land, however, was far from the thinking of the Congressmen a century ago when they visualized the people of Louisiana (and later the other twelve public-domain states) managing the swamps to control floods in the Mississippi Valley. It was their idea to build a system of drains and levees that would get rid of the fresh water as fast as it fell from the skies and thus keep agricultural lands dry enough to farm and relatively free of mosquitoes. Unfortunately, nearly all of the lands granted to the thirteen original states (and to Minnesota and Oregon) were transferred to private ownership whenever expedient, in payment for services that otherwise would have required tax money. Had this form of economy not been practiced, the Federal government would not now be in the position of buying back these "wastelands" at inflated prices.

It is easier to comprehend a conflict of interest between two agencies, or two people, than to see it in the mind of a single highly-trained individual. Yet this division was evident recently while we talked with a specialist on bringing water to valley farmlands in the southwestern states. His personal pleasure was in hunting in the forested mountains from which the water came, but for the good of the valley people he would have been willing to sacrifice his fun and the interests of the forester. To get all the water, he would have liked to see the high country completely cleared and cemented over, its water drained into covered cisterns of immense size. From these irrigation water could be drawn all year. We asked how he would handle heavy storms, which often drop more inches of rain in a few hours than any ordinary cisterns could hold. "Oh," he said. "That's easy." He paused to be sure he had our full attention, before continuing. "We'd line all of the present waterways with cement, eliminating every curve and bend. Then any excess rain would just run off quickly to the ocean, causing no flooding or erosion."

It is true that we have never yet tried to rest our eyes by gazing at a cement-covered mountain painted green to hide its baldness from distant view. But we have seen streams and wetlands drained through straight ditches, which are roaring torrents in storm time and often dry as dust in seasons of drought. Some of these streams come through the coastal cities of California, and disgorge into the Pacific. The engineers have lined many of them with riprap or with concrete, just as the water specialist dreamed. While walking along the beach we can pass the mouth of the erstwhile river without realizing that it is there. After each storm the coastal currents heal the beach together almost as soon as the outwash of water from the mountain slope is gone.

South of Los Angeles this change in the drainage pattern now affects a great many beachfront estates on which the taxes are enormous. Every winter the owners of the fine homes there see that the stretch of clean sand before their doors is narrower than the year before. In the spring of 1963, some of them banded together and hired investigators to learn the cause. Currents along the shore, they were informed, shift the sand southward little by little. Eventually it goes over the lip into a deep canyon from which no waves return it. This natural process did not show so long as new sand was being fanned out after every

storm by each river from the mountain slopes. But
without fresh sand the old beach material moves
along and the waves beat closer to the lawns. Now the
owners are paying to have dredges pump back the
old sand from the canyon floor, and to create diversion piers that may reroute the coastal current.

We recall, too, the straight ditches that were
dredged from one of the world's most magnificent
wetlands, the Florida Everglades. In the dark muck
below the marsh grasses, the real estate promotors
saw sites for homes near Miami and great tracts that
could be used for truck gardens, multiplying the
early lettuce and tomatoes on salad plates in colder
northern states. The new ditches they built hurried
to the Atlantic the fresh water that came with each
rain, and the water level in the marsh sank lower.
But the drying vegetation and the muck itself were
both flammable; soon fires raged or smoldered,
ready to break out again. Only by damming the
ditches and raising the water table could firemen
quench the embers.

Today an elaborate system of ditches, high walls
of earth, dams, and gates links all of southern Florida
from Lake Okeechobee to the Tamiami Trail and
the Atlantic Ocean. After every storm, a whole
series of adjustments must be made to keep everyone
supplied with just the right amount of water. The
truck farmers get first call if they are close to the lake.
After them come the users of domestic water in
Greater Miami.

For Miami residents the reflooding of the Everglades came just in time. Without the gravity head
to drive fresh water through the earth and out to sea,

the ocean water spread downward and transformed one after another of Miami's fresh wells to useless saline ones. To maintain this flow underground the water table in the broad marsh must remain reasonably high. For a while real disaster threatened most of the great estates along the shore. It seemed likely that the despised sea grapes and mangroves would take over because, without fresh water flowing seaward through the soil, the decorative royal palms began to die of salt poisoning. Drinking water might still be bought in bottles. But no one can create a stately entrance through an avenue of mangrove trees.

Elsewhere in the world, the cost of draining a large marsh or swamp has often been more than the economy would permit, and they have been left alone. Smaller wetlands close to large cities, such as Rome and London and Boston, have been obliterated by filling them with earth. This change did much to wipe out malaria, long before the *Anopheles* mosquito was discovered to be the carrier of the disease and its breeding pools were hunted out.

In regions of equatorial Africa where malaria still remains a serious threat to man, scientists of the new nations are taking a closer look at wetlands, to see whether the expense of draining them can be justified. Actually, very little is known about marshes and swamps, for they are awkward places to study. The *Anopheles* mosquito, to everyone's surprise, was found to breed in pools around the edges of wetlands, but not farther in. The number of disease carriers increases spectacularly whenever a wetland is opened up for development, augmenting the number of edge pools available to the insect. When marshes and swamps are left intact, the breeding places around the rim can be treated and the carriers of malaria brought under control without much cost or trouble.

The Africans are discovering that wetlands can be put to work at little expense, and without altering them as breeding places or wintering areas for fishes and migratory waterfowl. Substantial crops of food fishes can be raised in artificial ponds constructed by hand labor where water is in perpetual abundance. Following the lead of Rumanian industrialists, who are now experimenting with the reeds cut from marshlands in the delta of the Danube, it may be possible to harvest papyrus grass and other vegetation of permanent marshes as a raw material for manufacture of paper. This use does not lessen the attractiveness of the marshes for waterfowl, and might even improve them by letting in light and increasing productivity. In the headwaters of the White Nile, the seasonal marshes and swamps prove to be immensely important as nursery shallows for the many kinds of edible fishes that swim upstream in rainy season.

Some of these ideas can be applied widely—to the Everglades, the Sudd, and smaller wetlands all over the world. New practices would often promote the production of fishes, waterfowl, and perhaps fibers for paper and other uses, while safeguarding truly gigantic reservoirs of fresh water and mineral nutrients. The alternative, after draining a wetland, is frequently its abandonment after a few crops have been harvested. The valuable plants raised on the drained soil may transform it into an acid muck that is essentially sterile—supporting little of any importance.

In a sense, all wetlands are in a precarious state. Over most of the world they are merely a stage in the slow ecological changes that fill deep lakes with the rock crumbs from high mountains, converting both into flat meadows of deep soil. In some of our western valleys, between mountains that still stand, the sediments obliterating the lakes are seven thousand feet deep. By using radioactive trace elements, modern geologists have been able to prove that the water remaining between the sediments at the very bottom of those ancient lakes has been there unchanged for as much as ten thousand years—since soon after the end of the last Ice Age.

Floods and high winds bring the fragments down. The water catches them and holds them at its bottom. Gradually the lake is filled until the streams that formerly flowed into it meander slowly across its top between low banks of alluvial soil. To this extent, the men with bulldozers who push up a wall of mud and deepen a marsh are setting back the clock. Those who fill a swamp are putting the clock ahead. Neither can be sure that altering the natural calendar of events will do more good than harm.

Most of man's activities move the natural succession faster toward a stage with less fresh water. Each felling of a forest and draining of a wetland decreases the amount of water in the soil. Every time a stream or a river is converted into a straight drainage ditch, moisture hurries off the land before it has a chance to sink in and recharge the underground reserves. Often the debris from the original construction work, as well as dredged material that is removed at intervals from the bottom as siltation goes on, is heaped in great spoil mounds along the banks or used to fill adjacent wetlands.

At the University of Michigan, scientists have been keeping records for many years in an attempt to learn how fast the Great Lakes are filling with sedimentary debris. Now the rate seems to be increasing beyond the normal three inches a year, perhaps because of the discharge of industrial wastes and sewage from man's communities along the shore. Even the area of the lake in which the sediments accumulate is decreasing. Every few years the engineers build a new strong breakwater beyond the shoreline in front of a city, and then fill in the shallows between, producing more land and less lake.

Although the presence of modern man along the shore hastens the succession whereby a lake becomes a marsh or a swamp and finally level land, this process has been in progress naturally ever since the Great Lakes were formed ten or fifteen thousand years ago. Judging merely by the recorded accumulation of three inches of sediment a year, Lake Michigan—the second-deepest of these lakes—can be expected to become dry land in less than 3,500 years. Lake Erie, which is now only 210 feet deep, could fill at this rate in a mere 840 years. This is far sooner than the date that has often been forecast for the sudden draining of Erie into Ontario when the crumbling edge of Niagara Falls progresses all the way up the Niagara River at its present rate of about four feet a year. A time 27,000 years ahead has been predicted for this event, which is more than five times as long as is needed to fill the deepest of the Great Lakes—Superior.

No one need look 27,000 years into the past to discover a still larger lake of fresh water in North America. Less than 10,000 years ago, the melting ice from the great glaciers produced gigantic Lake Agassiz, which was almost as big as the state of Nevada. It sprawled across parts of Minnesota, North Dakota, Saskatchewan, Manitoba, and Ontario, and drained into Hudson Bay. Today its flat filled basin is spread with wheat farms.

The men who plan huge dams for flood control or hydroelectric power or irrigation recognize that they have no control over the length of time their reservoir will be useful. From the water it holds, sediments will settle and eventually transform it into level land. Often the men allocate the bottom half as a space to be filled before the value of the artificial lake diminishes seriously. This point is expected for Lake Mead by 1985, less than fifty years after completion of Hoover Dam on the boundary between Arizona and Nevada. The lake began with an average depth of 196.5 feet over its 247 square miles. That a fifth of the mud deposited on its bottom comes from the overgrazed reserve lands of the Navajo Indians in just one-fortieth of the water that drains into the Colorado River makes us wonder which is a better way to spend taxes—by building dams or preventing erosion by moving people and their livestock off marginal lands. In most parts of the country, reforestation is far cheaper than building dams for flood control, and provides a perpetual protection for the soil and for reservoirs serving in irrigation and production of power.

For transforming wetlands into land that is dry enough to cultivate and live on, no people in the world have earned so high a reputation as the Dutch. With the first hand-built dikes and wind-powered pumps they fenced out the saline waters of the shallow North Sea, and slowly rid the bottom soil of salt. It took a long time, because the Netherlands receive less than thirty inches of rain a year, and this had to be divided among many roles. Now the Dutch have become concerned over the smallness of the remaining salt marshes that might be used, and have set aside more than half of them as reserves. Still unsettled is the question of how much should be in fresh-water wetlands, and how best to use these for the good of the greatest number, into perpetuity.

As never before, international consultation and cooperation are making headway. Those interested in wetlands convene at intervals to discuss the future. In November, 1962, a group of experts met in a little village at the edge of the great Rhone Delta in Southern France. Around them was the largest of France's wetlands, the famous, mysterious Camargue. In it, much of Europe's bird life spends the winter, and wild cattle graze side by side with sturdy white horses. Afterward, the representatives from the seventeen nations looked carefully at another of the few remaining large wild areas in Europe—the marshes and dunes of Las Marismas near Cadiz along the southwest coast of Spain, long a favorite hunting preserve of the royal family. In both places, the delegates considered the possible values to be found in the wetlands of Europe and North Africa. Suggestions about management of these tracts came chiefly from the three countries that have already done most about fresh-water resources: the Netherlands, Great Britain, and the United States.

The sentiment that developed among the conferees seemed new. They foresaw less need for the dry fields that could be made by reclaiming the remaining wetlands than for the recreational values that the wild areas could generate. During the past two decades, the upsurge of interest in outdoor recreation has outstripped even the explosion in population. People are boating, water skiing, swimming, skindiving, and fishing in ever-increasing numbers. These activities are oriented toward water, and it need not be deep.

Despite the influx of people bent on recreation, the marshes and swamps still harbor a wealth of wildlife. By leaving these areas roadless, ditchless, and wet, man preserves a heritage for which appreciation is growing faster than the population in developed countries. The resource is solitude in the midst of life, where man can measure himself against the world in which his kind evolved. In a wetland, life is richer than in a dense forest, a broad plain, a great desert, or in any other spacious place to which man can retire to recreate his buoyancy of mind.

10

SEA FLAVOR

OF all the water in the world, more than 97 percent fills the ocean basins. Yet neither man nor the living things he particularly cherishes can use it undiluted. The animals cannot drink sea water, nor the plants tolerate it around their roots. From almost every kind of land animal and plant the sea is locked away by a seemingly trivial amount of dissolved salts. They accumulated there during the past few billion years, until the liquid became poorer in water than that in the living· cells of land life. Once in contact with these cells, sea water draws from them the moisture they need for survival.

Of the materials dissolved in the sea, six parts in every seven are of chlorine and sodium, so familiar to everyone when combined in table salt. Each element contributes in solution to the taste sensation we get from salt or from sea water. Together, as a fine dust produced by evaporation of salt spray, they provide much of the tang in sea air. When we inhale it and swirl some from our throat into our closed mouth, the dust reaches taste buds on the tongue.

Since long before the dawn of history, man has had a taste for salt. He has had to. It meant survival.

Although chloride and sodium comprise a far smaller proportion of the human body than of the sea, they can be depleted rapidly. On a hot day, as much as a tenth of the chloride and sodium can be lost in sweat and urine. Without delay this loss must be made good. To save himself, man has dug deep into the earth and mined salt from the remains of prehistoric seas. His womenfolk have boiled brine from salt springs to produce cakes of salt. Along the world's hot coasts and inland seas, people have labored in the sun to rake up a white slurry that would harden into blocks. In Roman times, each soldier fighting wars for Caesar's glory counted on a regular dole of money with which to buy salt. His *salarium* (salt money) is commemorated in monthly salaries today.

In the fifteenth and sixteenth centuries, legendary Timbuktu (now Tombouctou, near the Niger River in the Republic of Mali) was the prosperous cross-roads for great caravans winding across the southern fringes of the desert with crude blocks of salt. Until a few years ago, a procession of 2,000 camels journey-ed northward twice a year from Timbuktu for 450 miles to the Taoudenni Swamp in the heart of the Sahara, to haul out another 300 tons of salt and maintain the celebrated market.

In the open sea, sodium chloride does not exist. Instead, the waters contain charged particles of chloride ion (1.9 percent) and sodium-ion (1.0 percent). Neither of them, despite their concentration, acts as the real barricade to quenching thirst at which man falters. The barrier lies in two less abundant ingredients of the sea: sulfate ion (0.3 percent) and magnesium-ion (0.1 percent). These are the un-

absorbable ions that stay in the digestive tract when we swallow a dose of Epsom salts. If on any single day we drink more than a cupful of sea water, we get enough of these two ions to give the same effect. They prevent the large intestine from performing its normal role of salvaging water from the undigested residues of food. The diarrhea that follows robs us of water and leaves us thirstier than before. Magnesium ions at the tip and sides of the human tongue produce a salty sensation, but at the back an intensely bitter one, where the sense of taste gives its final warning before anything is swallowed.

In each 10,000 parts of ordinary sea water, these four ions account for 338 of the 345 parts of dissolved material. The remaining 7 parts are calcium, potassium, bicarbonate, bromide, boric acid, strontium, fluoride, and still rarer ingredients. Every chemical element known is dissolved in sea water. Believing that some of these trace quantities will be absorbed in meaningful amounts, many Europeans routinely drink a cupful of sea water daily. Pharmacies and health stores there sell the liquid in small bottles, its purity guaranteed. Perhaps this is "getting back to nature" for, on many a Pacific atoll and in arid areas where the only available water has a high content of mineral matter, people do drink somewhat brackish water and seem none the worse for it.

Those who seek to improve their health by drinking a cupful of sea water daily contribute almost nothing to the satisfaction of their normal thirst. Their human kidneys do not let them. Even when operating most efficiently, the kidneys produce a urine that is scarcely more concentrated than sea water. Each 10,000 parts of it contain about 380 parts of dissolved material, rather than the 345 in the sea. By the time a person has drunk a cupful of sea water daily for sixteen days, he has taken in a gallon—and gained from it less than a tablespoonful of water for his system. The rest has been lost again in flushing out the salts.

Only a person with a pair of healthy kidneys can slake his regular thirst with water that is brackish, with between ten and thirty parts of dissolved minerals per ten thousand. An indication of the number of unhealthy kidneys can be seen in the findings of the Census Bureau that in 1960 one person in each 145 who died in the United States succumbed to kidney failure. More would have suffered the same fate if it had not been for treatment with artificial kidney machines. And for each person using an artificial kidney, thousands are following a low-sodium diet because their kidneys no longer clear the body of the various dissolved substances that, if let accumulate, produce symptoms of disease.

Most people in America expect to be able to drink water as it comes from the faucet—as little or much each day as thirst dictates. To permit this, the U. S. Public Health Service limits what may be present in domestic supplies. Not only must there be no more than 750 colon bacteria per pint as indicators of pollution, but the dissolved mineral matter should not exceed 5 parts per 10,000—and must not exceed 10. This is in the same range as the tolerance of cultivated plants, and the U. S. Department of Agriculture recognizes 7 parts per 10,000 as the maximum that is acceptable in irrigation water.

All of the mineral components are not equally damaging. Calcium and magnesium carbonates, which make water "hard" and produce a curd with soap, may even improve the flavor. But to satisfy housewives who want "soft" water for washing, the officials at the municipal waterworks sometimes process the whole domestic supply by replacing the calcium-ions with sodium-ions. To do this is easier than to get the sodium-ions out.

Partly because of this practice, Dr. Walter Kempner of Duke University has recently followed up his pioneering work on low-salt diets in the treatment of specific diseases by recommending a separate limitation on the amount of sodium-ion in drinking water. His rule is twenty parts per *million*, which is a figure met by many communities that draw domestic supplies from active rivers or from deep wells. People on a low-salt diet who live where the water from the faucet contains more than twenty parts of sodium-ion per million are urged to drink distilled water instead. Even some bottled waters from springs contain more than Dr. Kempner recommends.

River water varies greatly in its mineral content according to the time of year. In autumn, the Arkansas River routinely reaches a concentration of 17.7 parts of sodium-ion per 10,000, and cannot be used for drinking no matter how well it is cleared of pollution by the water departments in Tulsa, Oklahoma, or Little Rock, Arkansas. The wells from which Galveston, Texas, gets its city water contain 3.5 parts of sodium-ion per 10,000 all year; newcomers often complain that it tastes like brine. Actually, water from the open Gulf of Mexico or from most of the world's oceans contains about 107 parts of sodium-ion per 10,000. Only a few wells are known that exceed this amount. Several, discovered by the U.S. Geological Survey in Kentucky, contain 311; one in Michigan has 667.

Unless the water we drink contains sulfate ion and magnesium-ion, or some other substance (such as agar) that competes with us for moisture, virtually all of the water we swallow finds its way through the walls of the stomach and intestines into the blood stream. Of the blood expelled by the heart at each beat, about a fifth goes to the kidneys, if they are normal. This is about forty times as much blood per pound of organ as goes to other parts of the body. Within the kidneys, the blood is distributed promptly to approximately two million microscopic filters. These present to the blood a total area estimated to be close to eight square feet. Through the filtering surface, the blood cells cannot escape. Neither can the fats or the largest of the protein molecules. But from the 1,800 quarts or so of blood that pass through the kidneys each day, roughly 190 quarts of filtrate escape from the blood stream. This fluid is collected by the ends of extremely slender tubes, one tube for each filtration center. Through the walls of the tubes, whose total length is close to 50 miles, the kidneys salvage most of the water and valuable materials in solution. By the time reabsorption is complete, all but about a quart and a half of fluid has been rescued and returned to the blood. The remainder is urine, containing the waste products and various substances in excess amounts in the blood. Some of them have been concentrated a hundredfold or more.

At their most efficient, human kidneys can produce a urine that averages about 4.2 times as concentrated with dissolved materials as is the plasma of the blood from which they come. This provides a generous margin of safety in supplying the body with the water it needs, so long as the solution we drink contains no more than five to ten parts of dissolved inorganic matter per ten thousand parts. It does not allow the Ancient Mariner or anyone else drifting on the open ocean to even partially slake his thirst from the half pint of sea water he can drink daily without causing extra water loss by diarrhea. Yet the shipwrecked man will soon die of desiccation if he continues to lose water—at least a pint a day for the minimum amount of urine formed, and three pints a day by evaporation if he is exposed to sun and wind. Nor is drinking urine any better. The kidneys are already doing the best they can in taking water from it. Sea water and urine are most valuable to the man adrift if he uses them to wet his clothing, cooling his body by evaporation. If he reduces his water loss in sweat, he can live a little longer and hope for rescue.

No one expects a man adrift on the open ocean to feel as relaxed as a baby in its crib. A physician examining him immediately after rescue would anticipate finding his blood pressure abnormally high, his emotional state not yet recovered from prolonged apprehension. These, like nervousness, are often symptoms of hypertension. So, in extreme cases, is inflammation of the kidneys (nephritis). We do not expect to find these conditions in an infant who is given the best of care. Yet, in a modern society, the child may be as limited as the man adrift, its drink and food containing more salt than its kidneys can handle properly. Cow's milk has long been known to contain 5.8 parts of sodium-ion per 10,000 parts, which is four times as much as human milk and in the marginal zone of safety for liquids drunk exclusively in place of pure water. Canned foods of many kinds sold for babies provide more sodium-ion than most foods eaten by adults. In northern Japan, where the salt intake of infants is the highest known, hypertension in adults is common and severe. These observations by a team of scientists at the Brookhaven National Laboratory led to investigation of canned baby foods in America. The strained vegetables, meat, chicken, and eggs from the supermarket, in cans prepared for feeding human infants, proved to have so much salt added that a child's health might be endangered, or the basis laid for hypertension in later years. A quart of cow's milk and 3½ ounces of these baby foods, if taken daily by a child weighing

15 pounds, would provide the equivalent of nearly an ounce of table salt for a 150-pound adult. This is between three and twelve times the usual amount of sodium-ion in a normal human diet.

A man adrift on a raft knows that his life is in danger, that thirst may be his undoing. He may try to catch fish and either squeeze moisture from the fresh flesh or get the water from the living cells by eating the fish raw. Just a single attempt to squeeze water from a chunk of fish muscle would end the first idea, for the juices are held most tenaciously. While trying to wring moisture from a piece of fish, a man generates more water in sweat than he gains from his work. Even a special fish squeezer with metal rollers is not much more efficient. Nor does the eating of fish flesh, either raw or cooked, improve the situation. After eating fish, people become thirstier than they were before, largely because of the extra proteins added to the diet. When proteins are digested and absorbed, additional wastes which contain nitrogen are produced and must be disposed of in the urine. A small amount of water, to be sure, is gained by the body through oxidation of the hydrogen in the protein. But it is nowhere near the half pint of urine needed to carry off wastes from each ounce of protein digested. Eating fish merely causes extra loss of water, worsening thirst.

All of the familiar foodstuffs—proteins, carbohydrates, and fats—yield both energy and water by oxidation. Proteins yield the least water, and lead uniquely to additional water loss from the kidneys. Fats provide plenty of water—about 1.1 pounds of it for each pound of fat oxidized. But the body seems reluctant to oxidize fats. Carbohydrates, such as starches and sugars, fit in between. A pound of water from each 1.8 pounds of carbohydrates is usual. They produce both water and energy most readily.

In trying to find ways to manage with human kidneys and less fresh water, we might learn to utilize moisture from our carbohydrate foods as efficiently as the kangaroo rats in deserts of the American Southwest. Once weaned, these amazing animals may go without a drink of any liquid for a whole lifetime. Carbohydrates are the mainstay of their survival.

At night, a kangaroo rat emerges from its burrow and jumps about among the cacti in search of the sun-dried seeds on which it thrives. Usually the animal does not eat its trophies immediately. Instead, it carries them home in dry, fur-lined cheek pouches, where the seeds can soak up no moisture from saliva. For many days the seeds remain within the burrow, during which they gradually absorb water from the air around them. The underground

environment has a slightly higher relative humidity than the air above ground, and this adds about 10 percent to the moisture in the stored seeds. When the kangaroo rat finally dines, it gains this extra 10 percent, as well as the so-called metabolic water from oxidizing the hydrogen in the organic foods the seeds contain.

A kangaroo rat is able to live on so little moisture, where a man cannot, because of its nocturnal habits, dry skin, and long nose, and because its kidneys are the most efficient known in the animal kingdom. By crouching quietly underground all day, the little mammal takes full advantage of the insulating power of the earth above its bedroom. It never encounters either the drying heat of the sun or the desiccated air above the sun-baked soil. Lacking sweat glands, it loses almost no water through its skin. By possessing a proportionately longer nose than man, it provides extra cooling for exhaled air between throat and nostrils. Its nose salvages much of the water that was used to humidify the inhaled air. And by concentrating its urine until the amount of dissolved material is seventeen times as great as in an equal volume of its blood plasma, it stays well within the amount of water produced by its metabolic economy. No other animal is so thrifty with water.

Virgil urged us to "Compare great things with small." In comparison with a kangaroo rat, a man is great in size. It would take almost five hundred of these little animals to weigh as much as a 160-pound man. To appreciate the advantages each kangaroo rat has in managing its water store, it would not be enough to think of one of these little rodents of the desert and one man, perhaps side by side, resting quietly on a comparable schedule of temperature and humidity conditions. We should think, instead, of enough independent kangaroo rats so that their combined use of oxygen per hour would equal that of the man. On this basis, the man would be losing water about three times as fast through his skin and lungs as all the kangaroo rats at once. He would lose four times as much in urine, and might marvel to see that the liquid voided by these rats often solidifies promptly, for it contains almost no unnecessary moisture. At the animal's body temperature, the urine is nearly saturated with dissolved wastes. Only a little extra concentration by evaporation or by chilling is needed to make them crystallize into a paste.

Free in the desert, a kangaroo rat avoids eating most seeds that have a high content of protein. How it tastes the difference and instinctively rejects them remains a mystery. But if a captive animal is given only dried soybeans, it will eat them whenever it is hungry. Soybeans are about 40 percent protein, and cause the kangaroo rat to produce more wastes that contain nitrogen, to discharge more urine, and to lose extra water from its kidneys. So narrow is its margin of safety without drinking that a mere two or three weeks on this high-protein diet will kill the animal by dehydration.

Thirst must be a strange sensation to a kangaroo rat. Yet, when one of them is already 10 to 20 percent underweight from water loss that has been induced on a soybean diet, the animal shows special interest in the succulent plants of the desert. If it is offered dew, it will sip repeatedly. Given sea water, it will drink—without harm or even diarrhea. From full-strength ocean water the kangaroo rat can replenish its body moisture and regain its normal weight. Yet it shows moderation, restoring its reserves at about a seventh of its body weight each day. This puts no strain on its kidneys.

When we come to think about thirsty man and thirsty kangaroo rats, we can appreciate how much longer these small mammals have had to become adapted so well to life in the deserts. Presumably they have been facing a chronic shortage of water for millions of years, whereas man has tried to invade the arid parts of the world only in the last few thousand. Still, some benefits might be found among his recent discoveries concerning the rats.

We too have metabolic water, gained without drinking. On the average American diet of three thousand calories a day (from about sixteen ounces of carbohydrate and three each of fat and of protein), we produce more than a half a pint of it. Another half pint of actual moisture in our usual foods would provide the minimum of water we require for urine. For better than this we can scarcely hope, since it would take many generations of directed evolution to change human kidneys until they could compete with those of kangaroo rats.

It would take time, too, and special motivation, to breed a race of long-nosed people, for there is no widespread realization that where fresh water is scarce the Pinocchios and Cyrano de Bergeracs have a real advantage. We might bear in mind that the Mongoloid race has the fewest sweat glands, the

Negroid race the most. But to save water, everyone in an arid land could follow the example of the kangaroo rat and live below ground, from soon after sunup until the ground surface and the air above it cooled off in the early evening.

With some slight modification, the bomb shelters which the citizens of America scorn—perhaps fatefully—might become the cool daytime residences of desert dwellers. The design could surely provide better ventilation than do the crude earthen hogans the Navajos build on their arid reserve. For the whole shelter, a substitute for the long nose of the kangaroo rat might be devised: it would humidify as well as cool the hot, dry air fanned in by day, and then re-absorb the moisture before releasing the air from the subterranean rooms again. This would decrease greatly our tendency to lose water from our lungs and to sweat. By taking our exercise only in the cool of the desert night, under the brilliant stars, we would again reduce our need for drinking water.

This pattern of existence would be far less confining than that aboard a submarine. It would allow people of arid lands to evolve in a new direction for man, as nocturnal beings. Most mammals already a-void the day. We ourselves are better fitted for seeing in the dark than the vast majority of night creatures. Only the horse, the various kinds of cats and owls, and a few less familiar forms of life see better now in dim light than we. All of them are color blind. As the new men of the deserts, we would still be able to emerge in time to enjoy the sunset colors, and to glory in all the splendor of the dawn before retiring to our underground humidifiers for the dangerously dry day to come.

If homes and offices were planned in the desert to gain the advantages a kangaroo rat finds in its burrow, no doubt the arrival of each thunderstorm would be announced by the ringing of bells or chimes all through the subterranean passageways, and by joyous announcements over the public-address system. People would hurry to the elevators and stairways leading to the surface, to watch pure water fall from the sky. Young and old would reach the open air in time to rejoice in the rainbow and the promise of fresh growth on the land around. For once—perhaps the only time in a year or two, since desert storms are so local and erratic—they could even dawdle a while in the unfamiliar brilliance of day. They might risk getting a sunburn while toying with the little runoff streams of water that soon would sink in or vaporize. Sometimes the kangaroo rats do this today, playing much as children do in the Tropics when suddenly a soft sheath of snow settles like magic over all the colors of the familiar scene.

In a sense, we cannot emulate fully the kangaroo rat for our own good, in an attempt to survive with less fresh water. We can imitate some of its habits, but not salvage from our urine so much of the moisture before it leaves the body. Millions of years were needed for the ancestors of kangaroo rats to evolve so extraordinary a mechanism for concentrating soluble wastes. We have no time for evolution to produce a comparable inner structure in human kidneys, making them correspondingly efficient. In this direction, the only substitute we might introduce would be devices to extract and purify the valuable water from human urine after it has left the body.

The ways of kangaroo rats may have changed far

faster than their kidneys, for the lands where these
animals live today were not deserts, but well watered,
during the Ice Ages only fifteen thousand years ago.
Their habits are still flexible, which accounts for
their ability to save themselves from death by desiccation if given sea water to drink—the only animals
that man, so far, has taught to take this salt solution
without harm. Flexibility of habit, rather than the
ability to drink sea water, is essential to kangaroo
rats. This is also true for the survival of mankind.

11

GOING LONGER WITHOUT WATER

MORE than any other large animal, the camels of
the Near East and North Africa have impressed man
by going without water for long periods. This justified respect began in the remote past, for the one-
humped Arabian camel or dromedary was probably
man's first beast of burden. Its bones are associated
with his in tombs dating from 5000 B.C. Perhaps,
in seeking ways to satisfy our own needs for fresh
water, a camel might be a better model to copy than
a kangaroo rat that manages without any water at
all to drink. Those who turn up their short, water-
wasting noses at the idea of emulating a rodent
might even recall Rudyard Kipling's story as to
"How the Camel Got His Hump."

Certainly the camel does go, like man and with
man, from oasis to oasis. Weighing a thousand
pounds, the animal is like man also in being too large
to burrow under the desert sands. Like the kangaroo
rat, it has a long nose. Its skin is usually dry. But for
centuries the peculiar hump or humps on its back
have caught man's eye as the clue to its ability to go
so long without water. Some people have assumed

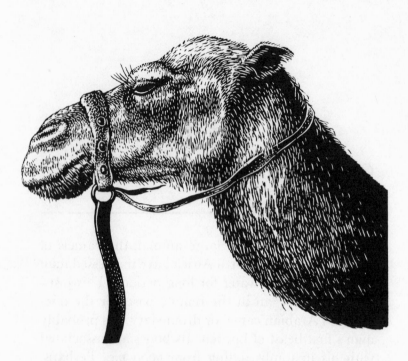

that the camel carries a reserve supply of liquid in its hump, or elsewhere inside its body.

Desert dwellers who know that a camel has no hidden hoard of water still marvel at the animal's readiness when thirsty to drink from bitter pools containing sulfate ions and magnesium-ions at a concentration high enough to sicken a person. A camel can browse on seaweeds, whose cells have as great a proportion of dissolved salts as are found in ocean water. Probably, although no one is yet certain from observation, a thirsty camel could drink sea water without harm.

To gain a scientific understanding of so remarkable an animal, Drs. Knut and Bodil Schmidt-Nielsen of Duke University began experimenting re-

cently with camels in the Sahara Desert. They learned that, in these arid lands, grazing camels are never
watered during the winter. The animals get enough
moisture from thorny bushes and succulent plants
on which they graze, benefiting from types of vegetation that capture and store water from any sporadic
storm. At any season, a man can manage equally
well without drinking, if he has a bountiful supply of
tomatoes, apples, citrus fruits, and similar products
of the plant kingdom. But he is no match for a camel
if deprived of his usual sources of water, or if he can
reach only pools with a high concentration of dissolved minerals.

When a camel goes without drink or food for day
after day on a journey, the hump on its back does
shrink. It is mostly fat, and contains very little free
water. But where the air is extremely dry the camel
simultaneously gains energy and loses moisture
while absorbing the fat in its hump. The fat there
may amount to 100 pounds, as a load offering about
110 pounds of metabolic water—more than 13 gallons. To get oxygen with which to oxidize the fat,
however, the camel must humidify the air it inhales.
Despite its long nose it loses more moisture than it
gains by the time the oxidation of the fat is complete.

Only in the cool winter season can a grazing
camel manage on the moisture it salvages from fresh
vegetation, supplemented by metabolic water. At
these times, it refuses to drink. The Schmidt-Nielsens
wondered whether by trickery they could upset this
perfect water balance and make a camel thirsty in
winter by giving it a diet abnormally high in proteins. They saw that animals rounded up from the

grazing lands enjoyed the hard-dried dates which are available in each oasis. Since the camel swallows the dates whole and later regurgitates the pits, the schemers decided to stuff the dates with peanuts. But most camels proved too sensitive in taste, and too conservative in eating habits. They spit out the loaded dates and refused to touch any more. When, finally, a few cooperative camels were found, the experiment came to an unexpected end: the supply of peanuts in the oasis gave out before the camels showed any sign of thirst.

Part of the camel's special adaptation to life on the fringes of the desert is its ability to spare its kidneys. These discharge far less waste that contains nitrogen and far less water than might be expected of so large an animal. While passing only a quart or less of urine daily—barely twice as much as a man— a camel can drag a load that would tire a three-mule team, over territory impassable to mules. It can carry a thirteen-hundred pound load for as much as ten days across the desert. Yet its ability to conserve water in its urine and handle those wastes that contain nitrogen is only one step beyond that of any other cud-chewing animal, and two steps beyond the matching mechanism in a man.

In essentially all mammals, urea is the nitrogen-containing compound that is the principal waste in urine. In water it is highly soluble and forms no crystals even when concentrated far beyond the amount present in an equivalent volume of blood plasma. Urea is a minor constituent of other watery secretions: sweat, saliva, tears. It is present too in the product of glands that line the stomach; it is there that the camel gains its special advantages.

All mammals benefit from the urea that they secrete into their stomach. The camel just benefits the most. In our stomach the urea merely protects us from digesting ourselves. Any area of stomach wall that fails to secrete urea along with a film of mucus is subject to attack by the digestive juice pepsin, creating a peptic ulcer. The digestive juice is active, however, only while acid. Continuously and slowly it spreads through the mucus toward the stomach wall, decomposing the urea in the mucus to ammonia. The ammonia neutralizes the acid, inactivates the digestive juice, and prevents formation of an ulcer. An excess of urea has no known effect, unless to reduce the rate of digestion in the cavity of the stomach.

If it were not for extra urea secreted into the first part of its stomach, a cud-chewing animal such as a camel or a sheep might well starve. The extra urea is needed, not by the cud chewer but by invisible partners—living bacteria which inhabit its paunch. Without these bacteria, the cud chewer can get little food value from the hay or other vegetation it eats. Hay is chiefly cellulose, a carbohydrate for which the cud chewer has no digestive agents. The bacteria *can* split the cellulose into molecules of lesser complexity. Thereby they render the cud chewer's meal much more digestible. But the bacteria seem chronically to be starving for nitrogen-containing substances, which are scarce in hay. The extra urea secreted by the cud chewer into its paunch gives a nutritional boost to the bacteria and spurs them on—to the cud chewer's benefit.

The exact roles of the partners in this digestive teamwork have been recognized only recently. The new knowledge has led to further improvements in the diet of important cud-chewing animals. The bacteria, though so essential, are never naturally allowed to work at top efficiency. They can do still more to benefit the cud chewer if the animal's diet is enriched with additional urea or even protein. Cheap synthetic urea and more expensive protein from fish meal now go into the feed for calves, lambs and dairy cattle. They speed the growth or increase the milk production by improving the nutrition of the cud chewers, without any significant change in the amount of food they eat.

A similar dietary supplement might mean little to a camel. Already this animal is secreting into its stomach an extremely large proportion of the urea it produces. Presumably the microbes in the camel's paunch have all the urea they can use; the extra must simply be decomposed by the stomach acid and passed through the digestive tract. So much urea goes into the camel's stomach, in fact, that far less remains in its blood to be excreted by its kidneys. A small volume of urine can contain all of the urea that is left, without becoming overly concentrated or expending much water. Freed of the ordinary burden of urea to be excreted, its kidneys have in reserve the capacity to discharge large amounts of chloride and sodium-ion when the camel finds seaweeds to eat, or when it drinks from a pool of salty water.

The unexplained tolerance of the camel for sulfate and magnesium-ions lets it surpass man in using almost any water it can find to satisfy its thirst. But the camel excels too at hoarding the moisture. It cannot avoid losses by evaporation through its lungs, but it does keep at a minimum the expenditure of water for cooling its body in desert heat. Its control over body temperature, its distribution of fat, and its coat of camel hair all contribute to this economy.

When a camel is denied access to water for a few hours, something changes in the thermostat-like mechanism in the brain, where its body temperature is controlled. Thereafter, until it can satisfy its growing thirst, the animal lets its body temperature go down as low as 93 degrees Fahrenheit in the cool of the desert night. Even if the camel were an inert bag of water weighing 1,000 pounds, the sun would take many hours to heat it from 93 to 105 degrees, which is the temperature above which a camel starts sweating. Up to that point, it has no need to spend water to save its body from growing warmer.

By having virtually all of its fat stored in its hump, a camel lacks the insulating layer found in human skin. Its blood vessels are close beneath the surface, and the heat generated by muscular work and glandular activity escapes readily from the blood so long as the surface of the skin is two degrees cooler. Without sweating, the camel lets its skin temperature rise to 103 degrees—two below the critical 105 in its blood. For much of the day, this is enough to insure rapid loss of heat to a cooler environment. By comparison, the fatty layers of the thinnest human skin retard the flow of heat from blood at 98 to 100 degrees whenever the surface of the body approaches a temperature of 93 to 95 degrees. The fatter the person, the cooler the skin must be to permit outward flow of heat; and the greater is the need for water with which to sweat and cool the surface by evaporation. When the air next to the skin gets into the range between 80 and 90 degrees, most of us begin to sweat.

Our astonishment over the wide daily range shown by the camel's body temperature is based on our own relative intolerance to variation. On the oral thermometer we count every fifth of a degree above or below 98.6—our "normal" temperature. In the course of a day, we seldom vary more than half a degree above or below this point. Greater variations may well signal that something is wrong. And if a person is chilled uniformly to 93 degrees—which means nothing to a camel—vision and hearing disappear. Below 85 degrees the temperature-control mechanism in the brain ceases to call for activities that might increase body temperature. A patient who is undergoing cold anesthesia in preparation for surgery is usually chilled to 77 degrees, just below the 80 degrees at which all breathing movements cease. The pupils are open wide, but all sensation has vanished. With surgery completed, the body temperature is raised by even heating. At 80 degrees the breathing movements reappear; at 90 the body thermostat takes hold; at 94, vision and hearing return.

Despite this intolerance for change, most of us enjoy a technological assist from air-conditioning when the summer weather warms us enough to cause sweating. On a hot day we feel refreshed by a cool shower or a plunge into a lake or surf at 70 degrees. All of these absorb heat from the body and save us from secreting water to accomplish the same effect. The strange feature is that people with so uniform

a blood temperature differ so greatly in their production of heat. Air-conditioning engineers have
found it impossible to design installations that will
make more than 50 to 65 percent of an average group
of people comfortable at any given season. The
temperature range in which each individual finds
comfort shifts markedly, moreover, with the season,
the latitude, the climate, and living habits. Heredi-
tary and racial differences seem less important.

The air-conditioner, the cool bath and the plunge
in the pool all save us not only water but energy as
well. It is work to sweat. This may explain the ability
of a workman to tolerate hot, uncomfortable surroundings all day so long as he can spend the night
where it is cool enough to need a blanket or two.
People who go to air-conditioned offices every day
benefit in the same fashion, for they can easily spare
the energy and moisture used by the skin from closing
time until the cool of the evening. Some are even
eager to get back to the office after a weekend of uninterrupted heat.

With a modern understanding of the role of water
in ridding the body of the heat it produces, we can
appreciate better the people who live in hot, dry
lands. Some of them show physical features that
match closely the camel's concentration of fat in a
hump. Two tribes in particular have become famous
for their fatty projections: the Hottentots and the
Bushmen, whose communities were once numerous
around the fringes of Africa's great Kalahari Desert.
Early travelers and missionaries told of primitive
beauty contests, during which a chief would line up
all the young girls in the village. Sighting along to

see which one projected behind the farthest, he would choose her as the winner—often of a place in his harem. The adjective *steatopygous* became a favorite in describing people whose buttocks showed special development. This aspect was more evident in photographs than the ability that went with it: to hike through the cool of early morning across a corner of the trackless desert, with only an occasional sip of water from an ostrich-egg shell carried in a cloth sling over the shoulder.

Today the Hottentots have disappeared as a tribe. Some were shot. Others blended into the melting pot of South Africa's population of Cape Coloured. The surviving Bushmen became the "harmless people," who manage skillfully to find subsistence in both water and food over parts of the Kalahari that are too dry and barren for anyone else to use.

A healthy Bushman of either sex wears in the prime of life almost all of the body fat in two firm pads high on the buttocks. Without scientific explanation, the young men of the tribal groups know that a prospective bride who has plenty of fat in these paired pads (and little elsewhere) can travel farther, work harder, and share more demands of nomadic life than one who lacks these signs of health and good nutrition.

Sometimes the word "steatopygous" comes to mind in a different setting, most often in relation to a typist who has sat too much. But the fat on her hips is not in high, localized pads at the back. Hers is an increase in the dimension that the physical anthropologist refers to as the "sitting width" or "spreadth." It does nothing to help her get along with a minimum of water or to tolerate the summer heat. It matches none of the adaptations found in a Bushman or a camel.

No matter how the fat is distributed, any person or warm-blooded animal must expend water to cool the blood whenever the air next to the skin is warmer than the surface of the skin itself. Only by doing so can the body be rid of heat generated within. And the faster the air we cool with sweat is reheated by air farther away, the more we must sweat. In this respect too, the flexible body temperature of the camel puts it ahead of man. Because the rate of heat flow toward the body is proportional to the difference in temperature, a camel with a skin surface at 103 degrees receives from desert air at 115 degrees only about three units of heat for every five units reaching our skin at 95 degrees. To match the camel's skin temperature, our blood would have to rise to a feverish 108, at which we would all be dead. To save ourselves, we dispose of the outside heat that reaches us by evaporating still more water.

We can conserve water by borrowing another of the camel's tricks. In summer, when the animal sheds much of its woolly hair, it keeps a thickness of several inches on its back. There the hair reflects a considerable amount of sunlight and slows further the transfer of heat toward its skin. Dr. Schmidt-Nielsen found that if a camel is shorn of its wool insulation it sweats about 60 percent more than an unshorn one standing in the same sun. The Arabian owners and drivers of camels have adopted a custom that closely parallels the camel's adaptation. Outdoors by day they wear six to ten loose burnooses made of wool. Englishmen and other Europeans prefer shirts and shorts—the least clothing that is legal in the desert. But they sweat like the shorn camels, while the Arabs under the burnooses are barely moist.

A camel can be denied the advantages it normally gets from its wool insulation and its ability to lower its body temperature during a cool night. The shorn animal can be kept in the sun all day and in a stable at 100 degrees by night. Still it shows how much better fitted it is than a man to go without water. The camel can continue to lose moisture in sweat, urine, and evaporation from its lungs until its body weight has decreased by more than 25 percent—more than thirty gallons of water. Still the animal gets around quite well, despite its emaciated appearance. Its blood will be decreased in volume by about a tenth, but be flowing freely, still bringing to the body surface the heat produced by muscles and glands.

Under comparable circumstances, a man produces more than a quart of sweat an hour, and becomes intensely thirsty. If his water loss exceeds 5 percent of his body weight (about a gallon), his mind shows the effect in distorted perception and faulty judgments. By the time two gallons are gone from his body, he is deaf, insensitive to pain, and delirious. He has left a bare margin of about three pints of water. At a deficit of 12 percent of his body weight, explosive heat death sets in because, unlike the camel, he has produced sweat largely at the expense of water in his blood stream. At the critical point, as much as a third of the water may be gone from the blood plasma, making it so viscous that his heart can no longer circulate the blood fast enough to get rid of body heat. Suddenly his body temperature rises, and death is quick. Only in cool surroundings can a man survive a loss of water amounting to 20 percent of his body weight.

As was so often noted during the past century, when prospectors for gold explored alone in the western deserts of America, the donkey often returns after the man dies of thirst along the way. A donkey tolerates a decrease in water amounting to as much as 25 percent of its body weight. It even outdoes the camel in replacing the lost water when given a chance to drink. In two minutes the donkey is back to normal. The camel takes about ten minutes. A man rescued at any stage of dangerous desiccation must drink far more slowly to avoid a hazardous change in the water content of his blood. One of the earliest stories of such a rescue comes from about forty centuries ago, when the henchman Sinuhe was felled by thirst as he crossed the Isthmus of Suez on a mission for the Egyptian king. He lived to write of his despair, with his throat burning, his tongue stuck to the roof of his mouth. "This," he told himself, "is the taste of death."

Like man, and unlike the camel, the donkey sweats freely in the hot sun. In all, the sweat is derived from blood plasma and resembles it in being more than 99 percent water. The salty flavor of sweat comes from the chloride and sodium-ion in solution. Upon evaporation these may accumulate in combination as a thin salt crust coating the skin.

Ordinarily the water in sweat is lost, just as is that in spilled tears, which have about the same concentration of chloride and sodium-ion. In the driest of all environments man has prospected, however, even sweat must be salvaged for reuse. America's first astronaut to spend several days rocketing around the world at stratospheric heights followed a plan that had been worked out in advance: into his tank of drinking water he transferred the moisture from his own body, as it was condensed in a special collecting vessel by the air-conditioning equipment built into his space suit. As needed, he could drink it without harm.

In the utter drought of interplanetary or interstellar space, man must rely upon his own forethought and technical excellence to survive. On his way to explore the moon or more distant celestial bodies, he may even begin to wonder about the wisdom of it all. It might be more feasible to invade earth's oceans, which are 97 percent water, than to colonize distant planets where water is lacking or extremely scarce. He might, of course, find strange forms of life on distant worlds and adopt their ways of surviving aridity before his own private supply of water escaped. But, without going so far, he has on earth a considerable variety of familiar nonhuman animals, even some with warm blood, among which to seek for ideas. As his personal share of fresh water grows steadily less, he may even be able to find better models to copy than the kangaroo rats and the camels.

12
LOOK TO THE SEA

"KNOWLEDGE of the oceans is more than a matter of curiosity," declared the late President John F. Kennedy when asking Congress in 1961 to double the amount of money to be spent on ocean research. "Our very survival may hinge on it." Now, more than at any time in the past, people all over the world are delving into the ways of existence of marine creatures, exploring the depths where most of them live, and looking for ways to make fuller use of the watery world.

"To be able to stay down in the depths, to work and live there in complete freedom, retaining contact with the water," became the dream of Commander Jacques-Yves Cousteau, co-inventor of the Aqua-Lung in 1943, co-author of *The Silent World* in 1953, and the director for some years of the fine oceanographic institute in Monaco. The technological competence was at hand, and in July, 1963, he saw the first stage toward having his dream come true. Seven divers completed a full month of consecutive explorations without incident, based in an undersea house forty-five feet below the surface of the Red Sea near the Sudanese coast.

Wearing the same black rubber suits and fins, waterproof goggles, tanks of compressed air, and other equipment that they had used every day for eight hours of continuous free swimming, they left their underwater doorway. Past the now-familiar contours of the coral reef, the men swam upward through the clear water to the sea surface and were taken aboard the research ship *Calypso*, anchored nearby. Another group of men, similarly attired, swam down by easy stages to occupy the submerged village. All of them had been there before as visitors, and were eager for the longer experience.

In planning and supervising this first colonization of the sea floor, Cousteau has even greater ambitions. His goal is the utilization of the margins of the continents beyond the shore. For a combined area of about four million square miles the continental shelves extend under the sea, before they drop off into depths greater than six hundred feet. This vast virgin territory is larger than the whole of Europe, as challenging as outer space, far more promising of economic reward, and the nearest part of the last real frontier on our planet. All of it has an abundance of sea water and a wealth of marine life, and lies a reasonable distance from the atmosphere.

While seven of Cousteau's "oceanauts" sleep, wash and shower, cook and eat their meals, and do indoor laboratory work or read in the five-room "starfish house"—whenever they are not outdoors at work in the underwater world—they receive compressed air from pumps aboard a companion ship, the *Rosaldo*. The pressure of thirty-six pounds to the square inch, which is more than double that in the

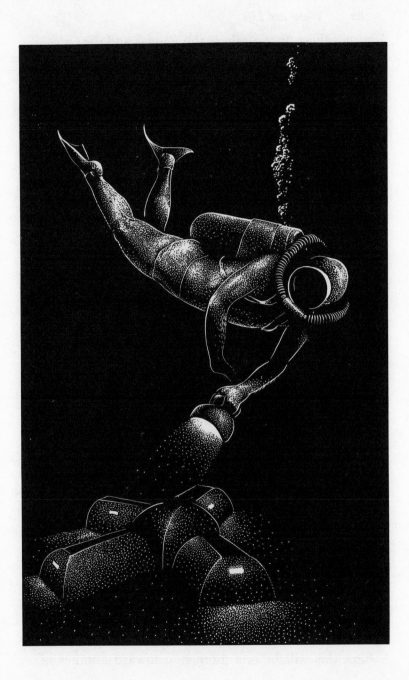

atmosphere above, where the *Rosaldo* and the *Calypso* float, is just enough to keep the sea from entering the open doorway in the floor of one room. Cables from the attendant ships bring electricity and telephone connections. Groceries are lowered in sealed cans, and supplemented by seafoods brought home by the divers. Fresh water comes through a flexible hose.

Centered near Shaab Rummi, twenty miles from Port Sudan (a land city with more than fifty thousand inhabitants), all of these activities seem a grand imitation of the silken diving bell that the water spider *Argyroneta* constructs in European ponds. But the spider, after stocking her bell with air brought down a bubble at a time, uses it only as a resting place between fishing expeditions. Cousteau's starfish house (so named for its shape) serves also as a way station toward still deeper levels in the ocean. After the oceanauts have become used to living and working at the 45-foot pressure, they take turns in going for a week at a time to a two-man metal house at the 90-foot level, on the edge of a sea cliff. From it they emerge for several hours each day, to observe marine life at the same and greater depths— to 135 feet below the surface, where the next part of the village is planned.

On a recent trip to Africa, we made the acquaintance of Charles F. Aquadro, M.D., who was joining Cousteau's staff as the full-time diving physician in this colonization of the sea bottom. Living with the men in the underwater village, he would seek to correct skin irritations caused by prolonged exposure to high humidity, and to find better mixtures of gases for the oceanauts to breathe at greater depths. Perhaps this will be one more step toward another of

Cousteau's dreams: to equip a free-swimming diver with artificial gills, and let him take his oxygen from the surrounding water as a fish does.

Although the success of the oceanauts in herding fishes has already raised the suggestion that future divers might become herdsmen of food animals in the deeps, no one seems to have seriously considered abandoning the hose line that brings fresh water to men below the surface of the ocean. If only men could live there without drinking, it might be much easier to colonize the continental shelves and the shallow lagoons, making the earth beneath the sea as valuable as the land in air.

Actually, man has precedents among the large mammals in the sea. The fossil record shows convincingly that, about fifty million years ago, the ancestors of today's whales and porpoises were four-footed amphibious animals living along the seashore. Almost certainly they preferred coastal foods, and escaped by swimming from land when attacked by predators, which could have included some of the last great dinosaurs. Soon, however, the cetaceans forsook the shore entirely and lost almost all traces of hind legs. Their fore pair became flippers, while the tail expanded sidewise into propulsive flukes.

Essentially all of the whale order solved the problem of living in the ocean without access to fresh water. Sea cows may have preceded them by a few million years in making this change, but the sea cows continue to be sluggish animals haunting the shore waters where the salinity is often much less than in the open ocean. The whales, by contrast, rarely leave the open seas and lead more active lives.

By rising to the surface only to breathe, the whales

and porpoises and sea cows all dodge loss of water by two of the three routes that jeopardize man on land. Three-fourths of our moisture is dissipated in sweat and through evaporation in the lungs. A sea-going mammal has no need to sweat. It may even benefit by some movement of water in the opposite direction, through the skin into the tissue spaces and eventually into the blood. The skin could serve as a dense filter, holding out the salt while letting pure water diffuse inward. If a frog and a toad can drink through their skin, as they have been shown to do from humid air, so may a cetacean in the sea. It would be a small adaptation, but one contributing a useful answer to the problem of fresh water away from land.

From immediately above the sea surface, the oceanic mammals inhale at each breath only air that is so nearly saturated with moisture that scarcely any extra water must be added by evaporation within the lungs. The great geyserlike discharge from the blowhole of a spouting whale is neither sea water nor steam. Instead, it is a froth of oil and air that protects the lungs from permanent collapse by the outside water pressure during a dive; it serves also as acoustic insulation around the deep-hidden inner ears while the cetacean echolocates its way in the black depths.

With only its water loss in urine to be compensated, a whale is under no obvious stress. By eating whole fishes, whole squids, or countless krill crustaceans that become trapped between the filter plates of whalebone, the cetacean again bypasses the difficulty encountered by a shipwrecked man on a raft at sea. The marine mammal digests not only the proteins in the muscles of its prey, but the carbohydrates and fatty oils as well. Unlike proteins, the other two types of nutrients carry no penalty in water loss for a mammal breathing humid air. A shipwrecked man could manage even better than a whale, if he could make himself eat only the raw livers of the fishes he caught. These would give him nourishment in carbohydrates and fats, without contributing much protein and thus also replenish his body water.

There is no rule, except habit of course, that requires a man on a drifting raft or in an open lifeboat to keep his feet dry and sweat from every pore. His inner store of fresh water would last much longer if he could avoid sweating altogether. In the Tropics, he might take a lesson from the porpoises and whales, by staying submerged in sea water. It would keep him cool and might drive a little moisture inward through his skin. A ship's carpenter has no difficulty installing a well in a sailboat, to keep water out while the centerboard is raised or lowered as a retractable keel. It would not be impossible to build a man-sized well in which a person could sit, as in a full bathtub. He would be protected there by the boat, immersed to the neck in sea water but safe from sharks. A much smaller shield would be needed to protect his head from the sun than to shade his whole body while he sprawls on the bottom. A life raft could be equipped in this same way, with a wet pocket for each person. People would ride in it, rather than on it, and contribute the natural buoyancy of human bodies to keeping it afloat.

Where the water at the ocean surface is cool or downright cold, whether in the Tropics or at still higher latitudes, it would be necessary to imitate another feature of whales and porpoises in designing a better life raft. The cetaceans conserve their body heat by a thick layer of blubber between the warm muscles and the skin. Even the thin rubber membrane of a "wet suit," such as now seems recognized to be the uniform of all skin divers, provides considerable protection. For survivors on or in a life raft, flexibility would be less important than conservation of body heat. But in guarding personal reserves of energy the need to safeguard body water would continue to be paramount.

Shipwrecked men and many others have often wondered about the considerable variety of birds that fly back and forth above the waves, spending weeks or months at sea with never a drink of fresh water. The gulls and kittiwakes, shearwaters and albatrosses, terns and tropic birds can all drink sea water. So can pelicans and penguins. No one knows how they avoid diarrhea from the sulfate ions and magnesium-ions. But they do have a special means for removing chloride ions and sodium-ions from their blood without burdening their kidneys. From the tip of the beak they drip away a salt-laden mucus that is formed by a special tear gland emptying low into the nasal passageways. The cells of the gland concentrate the secretion, salvaging the water in a way that no known breed of man can match.

If the human body cannot equal in tear gland or kidney the ability of other creatures in removing the salts from sea water and retaining the valuable water, at least the human mind can achieve the same end in the opposite way. Pure water can be obtained from a salty solution. One of the simplest devices that operates in this direction is one a shipwrecked man can tend, to save himself from death by desiccation. Now a standard piece of survival equipment, it consists of a one-sided greenhouse with a large plastic pane facing the sun and a tray he can fill with ocean water. Solar energy evaporates the water, which condenses again on the slanting pane and walls, there to run into a circuiting moat and collect in a storage bottle. The application is novel, but the principle has been known for centuries. In 1624 Sir Francis Bacon summed it up when he wrote: "With a heat sufficient for distillation, salt will not rise in the vapour."

Like a sundial, a solar still works only between dawn and dusk, and then whenever no thick clouds obscure the sun. Yet, even with uninterrupted sunlight and unlimited supplies of ocean water, the necessary area of the plastic pane becomes awkward. For each gallon of fresh water to be produced per day, the pane must have about ten square feet of surface if it is to do its work at 45 degrees latitude. Nearer the Equator, it can be somewhat smaller if only a gallon a day is needed from it.

In a sense, the energy for solar distillation of sea water is "free." But to use it at sea level to produce the 1,500 to 2,000 gallons a day per person needed to support a modern standard of living would require a capital investment of $15,000 to $20,000 per person for the collecting equipment alone. The famous fresh-water plant that has been operating on this principle at Las Salinas, Chile, since as far back as 1872, costs much more per square foot. It produces about six thousand gallons per day—enough for four or three people at the standard of living they would like. A smaller experimental plant built recently by the Office of Saline Water in Daytona Beach, Florida, yields only five hundred gallons a day. All of its output is measured and discarded, except for enough to fill a water cooler for visitors. Most who taste the product prefer whatever less-pure water they have at home.

Congress established the Office of Saline Water in the Department of the Interior during 1952. With financial backing totaling $75 million, the OSW is committed to supervise the preliminary tests (such as the one in Daytona Beach) as well as the construction of five demonstration plants, each with a daily capacity of 100,000 to 1,000,000 gallons of fresh water. At Freeport, Texas, and San Diego, California, and Wrightsville Beach, North Carolina, these plants are to use only sea water as the raw material. At Roswell, New Mexico, and Webster, South Dakota, they will pass brackish water through special filters that hold back the smaller amount of dissolved salts and let the pure water through.

To many people it seems incredible that so much equipment and energy should be required to purify sea water that already is 96.5 percent water. Yet wherever the salinity is as great as that in the open oceans, it is less expensive to get water from the brine than to take out the salt and leave the water pure. Already, the Freeport and the San Diego plants are operating, producing a million gallons each of fresh water daily. So pure is the product, in fact, that in San Diego it presents a hazard never before encountered by distributors of domestic and industrial water. Until it picks up twenty to fifty parts per million of dissolved mineral matter, the liquid is so ready to dissolve virtually anything that it is corrosive to pipes. To keep it from eating holes through the walls of containers, the hydraulic engineers now carefully mix the pure water they salvage with a small amount of uncontaminated river water. The mixture is piped to consumers, at a price of $1 or more per thousand gallons.

Price is a real obstacle. Currently the goal is pure water at no more than $1 per thousand gallons as it enters the distribution mains. This cost is within easy reach of the frugal householder for the comparatively small amount needed; present prices for the carefully pretreated liquid in domestic supplies average about 30¢ per thousand gallons. Industry is ready for the $1 charge, confident that the cost can be passed on to consumers in the price of the products; the modern average paid by industry for fresh water is about 2.5¢ per thousand gallons. Only the farmers see no hope in desalinized water at this price. For the immense quantities they need to irrigate crops in arid areas, they feel able to pay no more than 12¢ per thousand gallons, and this only for the most lucrative products of the land. Agriculturalists prefer to be charged 1¢ (which is common today) or nothing at all, after they have paid for putting in their irrigation system. At higher prices they doubt that they can compete with farmers on land with abundant rainfall and no need to irrigate.

A real "breakthrough," discovering how to make fresh water cheaply from sea water, would almost certainly earn its discoverer a Nobel Prize in chemistry and the highest award for promoting human welfare—both at once. But for such a leap ahead the prospects are less than bright. The stubborn fact remains that when salts are dissolved in water energy is released. To pry them apart again, more energy must be put in. Regardless of the process or the machinery it calls for, at least 2.98 kilowatt hours of work are needed to separate 35,000 parts of dissolved mineral matter per million from sea water and get a thousand gallons of fresh. To this cost must be added the expense of constructing and maintaining the desalination plant, and of distributing its product to consumers.

Even if the energy needed for desalinization could be supplied free, as an unsalable waste from some other process that cannot itself be operated more efficiently, the price of fresh water from the sea would be higher than could be afforded for irrigation. At present, an efficiency of 10 percent is about the best that skillful engineering permits; this implies a fuel bill for 29.8 kilowatt hours of power per thousand gallons produced. When we think of our electric bill at 7¢ a kilowatt hour, we can see that the water makers need cheaper power. Particularly is this true since, as Dr. Barnett F. Dodge, Dean of the Engineering School at Yale University, stated in 1960: "A 20 percent efficiency or 15 kwh per 1000 gal. is a possible goal but probably unattainable at the present time."

To many an engineer, the ideal process would be some modification of the solar still. Heat from fuel oil or a nuclear reactor could take the place of sunlight, producing steam from the sea water. The vapor would be condensed, cooled, and sold. They seek ways to accomplish this without having a layer of salt form as a scale on the heating pipes, blocking the transfer of energy.

Other engineers prefer a method borrowed from the Eskimos, who know that sea ice is almost pure water. The arctic people use the sea ice only after winter weather has frozen it naturally. When the freezing process is hurried, however, the crystals that form are small and coated with a film of salt water. Ice, instead of scale, may form on the cooling coils, blocking the transfer of energy. And the small ice crystals must be washed with fresh water to free them of salt, reducing the amount of fresh water gained for sale by melting the ice.

Whether the sea water in the machine is heated or chilled, the cost of warming or cooling the solution increases as water is removed and the brine becomes denser. It costs money continually to replace the raw material with more sea water, and also to pump the unprofitable brine out of the machine. At Freeport, Texas, the Dow Chemical Company is trying to find a way to reduce the cost of making fresh water in the OSW plant next door. By processing the concentrated brine still more, it may be possible to extract from it chemicals for sale. The gain would be considerable.

Where a community cannot live or earn a living without fresh water from the sea, almost any price for it is tolerable. Several dollars per thousand gallons means little to the oil-rich sheikdom of Kuwait on the Persian Gulf, where a fourth giant plant is being added to three that now produce 5,375,000 gallons of fresh water daily. The wealth in petroleum pays also for the world's second-largest distillation machine using sea water, at Aruba in the Netherlands West Indies. At Nassau, in the Bahamas, at Aden and Gibraltar and Thule in Greenland, sea-water distillation plants are basic to inhabitation.

America's first desalinization plant was installed at Coalinga, California. For years before this community had depended upon water hauled for forty miles by railway tank car, at a cost of $7.05 per thousand gallons. Since 1959 the residents have been happy to get cold sweet water from their own water lines at $1.43 for the same volume.

Today, a visitor can drive up to a water filling station in Coalinga, as he might to get his automobile tank filled with gasoline. The charge for pure water is only 2 cents a gallon, in your own container. It seems precious when bought that way. And then we think: 10 cents worth to flush a toilet once; 60 cents worth to take a bath. We shrug, for a 10-cent toilet is common in some cities of America. And we have seen the concierge in a Paris pension add to our bill an item of three new francs (60 cents) for each hot bath we took. We would not hesitate to pour 10 cents worth of fresh water on the earth around a treasured shrub we had planted—every day for a month, if this would get it well established. We have paid a dollar for a gallon of gasoline, too, for the luxury of having it waiting for us in the middle of an American desert, or a remote town in Latin America, or a dorp in the wilds of Africa. Now we wonder how much of the fare aboard the stern-wheel steamboat on the Nile

River in Uganda goes to pay for the precious liquid in the filter jar, above which is the conspicuous sign "Pure Drinking Water Is LIFE."

With such anticipation over drinkable water from the oceans, the words of Dr. Roger Revelle, Director of the Scripps Institution of Oceanography at the University of California, come back to us: "If all of the oceans were fresh water, it would still not do us very much good, because it is at such a low elevation." For thirsty cities and industries more than a few hundred miles from an ocean, as well as for the farmers on arid lands that are remote or high above the shore, the cost of piping and pumping is too great. For them, the rivers flowing downhill from the mountain peaks remain the fresh water that will sustain life.

Dr. Revelle's thoughts came from sea level. Those expressed forcefully by the distinguished anthropologist Dr. L. S. B. Leakey of equatorial Africa in 1963 provide a counterpart from a higher, drier vantage point. Speaking in Nairobi, at the triennial meetings of the International Union for the Conservation of Nature and Natural Resources, Dr. Leakey urged all of the delegates present to do everything in their power to prevent the diversion of fresh water from inland areas to coastal communities, which now could satisfy all of their requirements economically by demineralizing sea water. He cited the aqueduct built recently from Mzima Springs in Tsavo National Park for 150 miles to the Kenyan seaport of Mombasa. His comments apply equally well to water for Cairo and Alexandria, or Los Angeles and San Diego. Surprisingly, we heard no special applause from representatives who had come from Khartoum in the hot, dry Sudan or from Carson City, Nevada.

New ideas and practices in managing our natural resources seem inevitable if we are to get fresh water and food for tomorrow's human populations, let alone provide the inedible possessions that have become so important to modern man. Among our most incredible certainties today is that nothing short of a great calamity can keep the world from having 4,000 million people in 1980. This is 1,600 million more than there were in 1950. Like Alfred Lord Tennyson, we know that the necessary changes will leave as:

> . . . age to age succeeds,
> Blowing a noise of tongues and deeds,
> A dust of systems and of creeds.

Of the credos destined for the dust, one may well be our prevailing attitude toward coastal forms of life. In only a few parts of the world has anyone really tried farming the sea. And, of all the marine world, the coastal waters are the richest. Not only are they shallow enough for sunlight to promote the growth of plants, but dissolved minerals spread into them from the land and supply the nutrients needed as a fertilizer.

Thrifty Frenchmen have pointed the way to get tasty flesh that can be eaten any day of the week, before or during Lent, with never a need to supply the animals fresh water. By thrusting into the mud-flats just beyond the low-tide line a variety of branches and other objects upon which mussels will attach their threadlike tie lines, the shellfishermen encourage these mollusks to grow where thay can be inspected repeatedly and harvested when prime. No area on land produces so much protein per acre as a shellfish bed. Far more could be done to exploit this resource at moderate cost. And for those who balk at eating a mussel because its flesh is yellow, brown, or purple, a biologist might find an answer. It should be no more difficult to breed a captive strain of blond mussels than to produce a race of domestic fowl with white-shelled eggs.

In trying to conserve fresh water by developing food resources from coastal seas, the various shellfish have special appeal because of their high efficiency. The mussels and clams, scallops and oysters all filter from the water around them the microscopic sea plants which are the real producers—the equivalents in the sea to prairie grasses. By contrast, the large edible shrimp (which have recently been found to grow well in closed lagoons) eat smaller animals, which have in turn browsed on the microscopic plants. Efficiency diminishes by introducing an extra stage in the conversion of proteins from the producers to something people will eat. Similarly, the use of whale meat in human diets is still less efficient: a large part of the whale's diet is krill—an inch-long crustacean with feeding habits like those of the shrimp.

Now that billions of dollars are being spent toward travel aimed at waterless, foodless destinations in outer space, and lesser sums are being invested in villages below the surface of the sea, perhaps someone may soon build an artificial whale. Since its design would be free from the limitations inherent in the body of a sea-going mammal (one able to heal its wounds, grow, and reproduce), the machine might be constructed economically and do better than any whale at filtering protein from the surface waters. But the man who guides the monster will still have to follow a migration schedule matching that of whales, to harvest the sea alternately in the Arctic and the Antarctic. From the warm waters between very little is available despite the abundant light in every month. Except where the great currents cause up-welling of water from the bottom, bringing dissolved nutrients to the plants in surface layers, the sea is almost a desert. Acre for acre it produces on the average only a fourth as much protein as the land. Its open waters offer little for exploitation that would benefit hungry men.

Today the controversy over dried protein meal made from whole marine fishes, and over the incon-sistent rules as to what is clean enough for human food, often conceals some actual facts of economic life. The people who need the protein most have so little money or basis for barter that they cannot support the fishing and processing industries which have fish meal to sell. Only in the more prosperous nations, where the amount of protein in the average diet is fairly satisfactory, can people afford to buy the processed meal—and to feed it as a supplement to livestock and pets. Although millions of mankind suffer from malnourishment, particularly from in-sufficiency of protein, their needs can probably be met more cheaply from their own land, even if pro-ducing the extra food there requires a greater expend-iture of fresh water.

Many avenues to extra food from coastal life are

still open, without increasing the demands upon
lakes and rivers, or upon fresh water in wetlands and
underground. Caesar's cavalry horses fed well on a
hay of eelgrass cut for them from Mediterranean
shallows during his campaign in North Africa. Many
a New England farmer has kept his cows on salt hay
that was raked from his coastal marshes. These
practices rely on land plants that have become well
adapted to living in brackish or salt water, yet filter
out the salts in a way that man has not yet learned
to match. Wetlands along the seashore could be
developed to yield safe, nutritious fodder for livestock
far more reliably than any alfalfa field that is beyond
reach of cheap irrigation or abundant natural rain.
To do so would require no more engineering than
now is spent on building roads into these marshes
so that dump trucks can fill them with garbage. The
garbage would have to be disposed of in some other
way, but the saving in fresh water and the gain in
food might be worth it.

Obliteration of coastal marshes, and pollution of
many that remain, account for a considerable part
of the decline in marine fisheries offshore. These
marshes have been the nursery grounds for young
fish, either of those we would like to eat or of smaller
kinds on which the larger feed. In addition, the
natural flow of water from the land to sea flushes
from coastal marshes a wealth of food for ocean fishes
and lures them toward shore where they are easier
to catch. If fisheries received a public subsidy comparable to that now going to the farmers on arid
lands, the supply of fish would rise rapidly with almost no expenditure of fresh water.

Along coasts where frost is no hazard, another

type of meat is available for future development—
if it does not become extinct before the surviving
animals are used to augment the resource. Particularly around the Caribbean, the great sea turtles
come ashore to lay their eggs deep in the sandy
beaches. Otherwise they feed in greater safety among
the turtlegrass of more remote shallows, and on seaweeds growing in quiet waters. Under the leadership
of Dr. Archie Carr of the University of Florida, vigorous attempts are now in progress to improve the
nesting beaches and to protect the mother turtles.
With a little encouragement the turtle population
seems likely to grow instead of shrink, and to yield
large amounts of valuable meat for hungry men.

Equally threatened and seldom appreciated is a
still larger beast in estuary waters, as far north as
southern Florida: the great sea cows (manatees)
which browse at night on the more succulent water
plants. If unmolested, these sluggish mammals attain
in a few years a weight of as much as fifteen hundred
pounds, much of it a soft and delicious meat. The
sea cows produce it at the same time that their
browsing keeps waterways open; without their help
man spends thousands of dollars on trying to control
water hyacinth and other vegetation that luxuriates
in these brackish waters.

Whenever we discover a sea cow in Florida waters,
we wonder how well a ranch of shallow lagoons for
them would fare. The same dragline equipment that
is used to make a seemingly endless network of
canals, so that every lot in a development can boast
a boat dock, would suffice to make a place for sea
cows and the plants they eat. They would need pro-

tection from the keels of boats, and from people who would prefer to speed over them on water skis. On frosty nights they would require about the same care as an orchard of citrus fruit. But no one would have to water them. And the yield per acre would probably be higher than for beef animals standing in the Florida sun.

For a while, at least, a ranchful of sea cows would be a greater curiosity than a pastureful of domestic cattle. Yet these native animals, which can either drink from the sea or manage without drinking, might well add to human welfare at far less cost than is spent per pound for protein where the supply of fresh water is now so short.

13

NEW WAYS FOR OLD

To a degree greater than we usually realize, to-day's diet reflects man's past preoccupation with well-watered lands, with lake margins, river banks and flood plains. Now that the amount of food that can be raised in these limited areas of the continents is less than the world's human population requires, it is time to look again at our dietary customs. Without much loss, it may be possible to place greater emphasis on things that grow with less water.

Water is one of three things that are hard to come by on the high plains of central Africa. It and the other two—nourishment and salt—are all ingredients in a Masai cocktail. Yet, to most of the world's peoples, this potion represents the very peak of the primitive. To prepare one, a hollow gourd is dried and sterilized inside with a handful of ashes from a fire made with straw and dry dung. After rinsing out the ashes with human urine, the two real ingredients go in. Both must be newly drawn, still warm: fresh cow's milk and beef blood. Shake well, and drink. Even the emerging Africans look askance at their equatorial kinsmen, such as the Watussi and the Masai, who have been thriving for countless generations on this mixture.

Some of our own European ancestors included in their diet a spicy "black sausage" made with beef blood, stuffed into a "sausage casing" made from a cleaned length of intestine from a sheep, hog, or beef animal. Their blood pudding had no fancy name to disguise its nature. Many in America prefer to forget about these inexpensive, traditional dishes, which are still sold in cities; they care nothing about the nutritional values each contains. A number of people have expressed themselves as being strongly against the addition of blood to hamburger because they felt it to be an undesirable impurity, rather than because the butcher was using it to hide the white fat for which he wanted to charge the fair price for red meat.

Today the scientists of the world can see in a Masai cocktail or a blood pudding a valuable part of the heritage that has come down from the distant past. Dietary customs conceal a wealth of empiric discoveries made by early man. Some of them, such as the drinking of blood from cud-chewing animals, were once the stuff of survival. This particular specialty replaced the chloride and sodium-ion lost in sweat by people who had no other source of sodium chloride. Without knowing why, they followed custom in choosing the blood of herbivorous animals that traveled annually for many miles to salt licks. With the advent of the salt trade, most of the reason for the custom vanished. Among people who did not know why the ritual arose in the first place, no reason for abandoning it was seen either.

Before the good in primitive customs is lost through the universal adoption of newer usage, the significance of the old ways should be discovered and given a fair consideration. Unfortunately, almost as much care is needed to separate real remedies from pure superstition as goes into making new discoveries about which there is no aura of confusing beliefs. At a time when knowledge and understanding of the world are growing like the area of an expanding circle, the new frontiers around the perimeter—against unknowns that could not be recognized before—often seem more inviting than the tribal rituals of primitive men who may soon be extinct.

Even from the broad stage now so occupied by modern science, it is sometimes hard to get perspective on the ways we follow. Perhaps the best route to a fresh viewpoint is the one we have tried a few times: spend a while among primitive people, and then return to civilization. Just as the trees of New England take on a strange and unfamiliar shape after a few months in the Panamanian rain forest or on the savannas of equatorial Africa, so too the choice of familiar foods in the Western World becomes subject to question after living elsewhere. Why roast beef and potatoes? Or rice and beans with chicken? Or suckling pig and poi (taro)? These differ little in nourishment from mealies (cornmeal) and stewed weaver birds; or spaghetti and thick meat sauce; or rusks baked from wheat flour and a stew made from dried strips of antelope or ostrich (whichever the hunter happened to get).

Before the food habits of our childhood settle a-round us again like a comfortable coat and smother our sense of contrasts, we may think of the origins of familiar foods. Many of them were adopted so long ago that no dates can be assigned. A few seem touched with legend, such as that Alexander the Great brought back from the Far East a taste for bananas, and some banana plants, before he sat down to cry over a lack of more worlds to conquer. In all recorded history, no comparable length of time before or since the fifteenth through the seventeenth centuries A.D. seems to have seen more unfamiliar vegetables and fruits, beverages and cereals adopted in new lands.

In South Africa we asked what the Negro people used in pre-Columbian days, in place of Indian corn ("mealies"). The answer was millet, a cereal of the very poor still in some parts of Africa, as in the Near East and China. African crops of millet are sold extensively today to buy bicycles and sewing machines; the seed turns up in the food cups of cage birds all over the civilized world. We wonder what the Irish ate before 1600, when the potato was introduced to the Emerald Isle from South America, by way of Spain and Germany. Were water and alcoholic beverages the mainstay of Europeans before the sixteenth century, when coffee houses and tea took over? A salad is scarcely imaginable until a tomato from Latin America got together with a lettuce leaf from Asia Minor—a prize brought to Rome in the days of the Caesars.

Far more can be seen in a list of foods than their places of origin and the probable dates of their adoption or spread. Most, although not all, of the things we eat are products of lands where water is abundant. Few indeed come from dry-land agriculture. But now more than two-thirds of the world's population lives in nations that literally starve for water—where famine due to water scarcity or malnutrition of the same basic origin causes more deaths than cancer. Where the soil is starved for water, men starve too.

That a change from this situation will not be easy can be seen in the fact that more than half of the world's people depend today chiefly on rice, which is cultivated under artificial conditions equivalent to a marsh. All but a twentieth of the world's rice harvest is raised and consumed in the Orient, where each person eats from two hundred to four hundred pounds of it a year if he can get it. According to census information released through the United Nations in 1963, rice eaters in the Far East and Latin America are consuming rice as never before. They are also increasing in numbers faster than the exploding populations of people who rely upon wheat or corn, potatoes or taro. As the sun sets each night, the world has about 150,000 more human mouths to be fed than there were the night previously. Of these, about 100,000 newcomers will want wetland rice.

Already the annals of science show what can happen when rice eaters are ordered to change to a substitute. Suspecting in 1882 that a monotonous diet of polished rice might have something to do with the large number of Japanese sailors suffering from the mysterious disease called beriberi, a naval surgeon (Admiral K. Takaki) arranged for an experiment on two warships that were being sent simultaneously on long missions at sea. Aboard one went the usual amount of polished rice. The stores of the other vessel included so little rice that a tight system of rationing had to be instituted immediately. For a reason unknown even to the officers, this rice-short ship was well supplied with barley, vegetables, condensed milk, and meat—far beyond the usual amounts on a Japanese ship. These the sailors received in place of rice.

Of the 276 men aboard the vessel with the normal amount of rice, 169 suffered from beriberi, and 25 died during the mission due to the strange disease. Aboard the experimental warship, no one died of it, and the 14 men who showed symptoms of the disease were the few who tried to live on what little rice they could get rather than eat the unfamiliar diet. Thereafter all Japanese sailors were required to follow the new diet, and among them the death rate from beriberi fell from 17.29 to 0.64 per thousand.

During the eighty years since Admiral Takaki's experiment, the cause of beriberi has been identified as an insufficiency of thiamine—vitamin B_1. This material, which is removed during the polishing of rice to make it white instead of brown, is available now in synthesized form as one of our cheapest supplements. One milligram of it, costing less than a tenth of a cent, is all a human body can use each day.

In Japan, cheap thiamine and a recognition of its importance are widespread. More people than ever before learn about it in school. But dietary preferences lead them to ignore it. In 1957, the Welfare Ministry noted a sharp rise in the number of people suffering from beriberi, and attributed it to four consecutive years of peak production by rice farmers. Paradoxically, a bumper harvest of rice there leads to malnutrition. With more rice available, people turn away from proteins, fats, vitamins, and minerals.

Already much of the gain has been lost and more than one person in four is suffering from this deficiency disease. A postwar trend has been reversed, one that came partly because of shortages of rice and partly through dietary reforms introduced during the occupation. The human growth rate, which was highest in 1955, is dropping. Among rural children, who consume more rice, the average height at ages of ten and under is now between one-quarter and three-quarters of an inch less than among city children of equal ages.

In the United States, despite production of so much rice that governmental controls have been applied, people buy less than six pounds of it apiece each year. Not all of this is eaten, for a considerable amount is pelted dry at newlyweds, wasted in a fertility rite imported long ago from the Far East. The bulk of American rice is shipped overseas, at prices that can undersell even the notoriously cheap products of coolie labor in the Orient. The efficiency that makes this possible rests on controlled irrigation and mass production.

The nature of the rice plant limits its culture almost completely to warm, wet parts of the country: Louisiana, Arkansas, and some parts of coastal East Texas, together with portions of the Sacramento Valley in California. In some of these areas, planting is done by mechanized equipment driven along the ground, starting the crop in close-set rows. In others, the seed is broadcast from airplanes flying low over the wet ground. Fertilizing and weed killing can be accomplished cheaply from the air. The only time a man is on the rice field, in fact, may be when the heads are ripe and the land let briefly become dry. Then he guides harvesting machinery which cuts, threshes, and bags the rice, after which he uses plows and other cultivating devices to prepare the land for its next crop.

When grown with plenty of water and fertilizer, in ideal climate, and with careful control of weeds either by chemical means or hand labor, rice is man's most productive food crop. Enough of it can be grown on a square mile of paddies in a year to support 1,538 people who eat little else. But where no irrigation water is added to supplement the rain that falls (as in some rice fields in the United States), or where farming methods are primitive (as in many parts of Latin America), the yield of rice falls off to about a tenth as much. This favorite of the world's cereals cannot compete with wheat if it is grown as "upland rice."

In considering rice from the vantage point of a land where wheat is king, we enjoy a perspective not found in much of the East. Robert Burns longed for this view when he wrote:

> Oh wad some power the giftie gie us,
> To see oursels as others see us!
> It wad frae monie a blunder free us,
> An' foolish notion.

Because of our experience with wheat and with crops other than rice, we are automatically critical of the water requirements of each type of food. We may say that a square mile of the earth's warmer continental areas will provide enough meat in a year for 64 people, or milk for 725, or wheat for 950, or potatoes for 1,220, or corn for 1,340. In each case we are visualizing the pasture or field with just the right amount of water, the best climate for that crop, the proper soil, and adequate care. We may lump all of these in the phrase "Under the best circumstances." Of all these crops, only the wheat can be sustained at high yield without irrigation on land where the annual rainfall is less than thirty inches. With more rain, wheat does not grow well.

People in the United States consume about 121 pounds of wheat apiece each year, essentially all of it in products made with flour. We accept that our custom depends upon powerful machinery for grinding the wheat, and suitable fuel for an oven in which the dough can be converted into baked goods. Natives of the Orient do not know what to do with wheat since, unlike rice, it cannot be made palatable merely by tossing it into a pot with a little water and boiling it a while. In the Far East, where essentially all of the forests have been cut to make space for rice fields, fuel is too expensive to use in the quantities required for keeping an oven hot. A whole way of life has developed into a fixed pattern around this fact. It requires almost no machinery. To anyone in the Orient, the statement that "Bread is the staff of life" makes little sense, whereas to a Westerner the invention of bread about 4000 B.C. in Egypt seems a real landmark in the development of civilization.

A counterpart can be recognized in the pattern of Western life. Since only the grains of wheat and rye contain enough of the protein gluten to hold together in baked goods, rice seems almost useless—a novelty in the diet, rather than a staple. After World War I,

Herbert Hoover found that the Belgians who were starving would rather go hungry than eat the rice we could send them. After World War II, the Germans politely declined an offer of corn for the same reason. During the occupation, the Japanese refused to try corn. No matter how hungry, people are unwilling to venture upon a cereal that requires totally different methods of preparation. Yet, if made from the whole grain or enriched deliberately, the dishes made with rice, wheat, rye, and corn are more alike than different in nutritional values. The greatest discrepancies among them lie in the amount of water that must be available to raise each as a crop.

When viewed as impartially as possible, diets all over the world are similar. Something spicy, meaty, cheesy, or sweet goes with a basic bland food, which may be boiled rice, bread, corn mush, mashed potatoes, or poi. The bland components differ in texture and subtle flavor, and provide most of the carbohydrates which will be converted into energy after digestion and absorption. They constitute the real bulk of each meal, and test to the limit a person's tolerance and versatility when changing from one culture to another.

On our first expedition into the American tropics, we found the Panamanian diet of rice and beans increasingly monotonous, with no help from the substitute for bread—the pancake-like tortillas, made from ground corn. We tired of the flavor of black beans, of the texture of the rice, and of tortillas upon which no one put butter or jam or anything else to add interest. Only the variants in each meal proved delightful: the chayotes, fried plantains, papayas, avocados, meat of iguana lizard, and the like. Yet, no matter whether we ate with wealthy people or really poor ones, the rice and beans and tortillas were the staple—just as spaghetti from hard wheat would be in Italy.

As our experience grew we began inquiring: "If you were to go into the best restaurant or hotel dining room in the country, with your meal paid for no matter what you ordered, what would you choose?" Naïvely we expected to hear: "The biggest, juiciest, tenderest steak in the house!" Never did this response turn up. Instead, the answer invariably included beans, rice, and tortillas, with quality the principal goal. Eventually we began commenting that to us it seemed strange for such emphasis to be put on vegetables and a counterpart to bread. This observation surprised our Panamanian friends. To them black beans were not a vegetable, but almost a meat.

After we thought about this a while, we realized that American menus often accompany the choice of entrée with bread and butter, potato, and a vegetable. To the writer of the menu and to the waitress, potato stands apart in a category higher than any mere vegetable, and classed with bread and butter as a necessary feature of the meal. On many tables, potatoes appear three or four times a day, along with bread. They match perfectly the rice, beans, and tortillas.

Often we do not realize how much the availability of water alters both the food used and the way of dining. Except in the United States and Canada, a glass of water does not come automatically to each place setting, along with the silverware, bread, and butter. Once, while having a meal in the main dining room of a large hotel in Johannesburg, South Africa, we asked the waiter to bring each of us a glass of ice water with our dinner. It didn't come, and we reminded him. "Yes, yes. It will be here presently." We reached the dessert, and still no water—despite a boast in the descriptive leaflet of the hotel "The water in every room of our hotel is safe to drink." To test the service, which had been so uniformly gracious, we held out, and finally were rewarded. A special waiter arrived with two glasses of water with ice on a tray. As he set them before us with a flourish, he apologized for the delay. The only place in the hotel, it seemed, where water and ice were available together was in the bar. And before us no one had ever got anything from the bar without paying for it. The manager of the hotel had to be located to allow this special favor, humoring the visitors from America. Please accept the ice water with the compliments of the hotel!

Water may be too scarce to waste on people who would leave untouched a glassful set before them, even where the water from the faucet is safe to drink and the rainfall is right for growing wheat. Johannesburg receives 33 inches of rain a year, but almost none in the dry season. Our own state of Mississippi gets between 50 and 64 inches annually, with at least 2 ½ inches every month. Yet crops in either place benefit from extra water whenever the soil shows signs of getting dry. An official publication on water by the United States government told in 1955 what a farmer could expect in increased vigor and productivity. In Mississippi, 20.6 tons per acre of millet (wet weight) were harvested under irrigation, but only 8.9 tons without extra water. An acre of Irish potatoes yielded 28 bushels with neither extra water nor fertilizer, 162 bushels with no water but the best fertilizer, and 229 bushels when both irrigation and fertilizer were perfect. This response among plants was immortalized in 1656 by Abraham Cowley, the English poet, when he wrote:

> The thirsty earth soaks up the rain,
>   And drinks, and gapes for drink again.
> The plants suck in the earth, and are
>   With constant drinking fresh and fair.

Today's farmer sees poetry in the statistics on his crops. If his farm lies in the subhumid zone, rather than in a rainy part of the earth, he can count on about twice as much from irrigated land as the average without extra water.

Before use of irrigation became so widespread, alfalfa had already taken a leading place among the plants man raises as food for cattle. Being a legume, with nitrogen-capturing bacteria in nodules on its roots, it benefited the soil. And its roots reached deeply to moisture, allowing it to grow vigorously through periods of mild drought. But when measurements were made on alfalfa, it was found to use water more extravagantly than almost any crop man raises —except for wetland rice. To produce a ton of alfalfa hay takes as much as 900 tons of water, whether by irrigation or from rain. When the alfalfa is fed to cattle, the animals need additional water, raising the cost of beef to about 30,000 pounds of water to each pound of beefsteak.

By eating a plant product directly, rather than at

second hand in the form of meat, man is much less demanding of water. A pound of potatoes represents only 636 pounds of water absorbed by the plant, a pound of wheat 500, and a pound of corn 350. In each instance, all but about three-fifths of a pound of moisture is lost by evaporation into the atmosphere in making each pound of plant. None of these crops, however, approaches the economy of a cactus, which can produce a pound of cactus with only 40 pounds of water captured from a desert storm.

In those parts of the world where an abundance of water is giving way to impending scarcity, the need for a matching change in the pattern of living is now evident. Less apparent is the possibility of an adequate diet for those people who inhabit parts of the world in which the supply of water is chronically inadequate, or those where the population far exceeds the total that can be supported by plants such as wetland rice, for which an abundance of water is essential. The real question is whether people can be induced to change their eating habits and their goals in production of food at the pace that will be required by the growing imbalance between the world's population and the world's supply of fresh water.

Always it seems easier to see what needs to be done in a distant land than to recognize the best action close at home. In equatorial Africa, the upsurge in human population and in the number of domestic cattle during the past few decades has been so spectacular that many causes of the change stand out. Probably the police action of the colonial powers, in suppressing intertribal wars and slavery of Negro to Negro, accomplished a little in prolonging life for the native people. Diseases remained the real check on population. But the introduction of medical and veterinary care, particularly with the use of vaccines and antibiotics, worked wonders. People and their domestic animals took on unfamiliar health. The death rate shrank amazingly, but not the birth rate. With more sons surviving, for whom a father would need to buy wives with cattle received in exchange for his lively daughters, and with more calves maturing too, the number of cud chewers doubled and doubled again. The fodder available has not increased, nor has the supply of water.

Looking ahead only a decade or two, the most expedient way out of the present crisis is to turn over to the herdsmen the forage and waterholes of all reserves for wildlife in equatorial Africa and highlands farther south. This would be a desperate gamble. It could succeed only if, by the time these areas are ruined by overgrazing, science will have found a way to change the weather and bring rain to the high plains. Without some discovery akin to magic in the next few years, the remaining parklands would surely be drunk dry and pounded to desert under the hoofs of still more cattle.

The domestic cow and bull, which are *Bos taurus* to a scientist anywhere in the world, originated from a race of wild progenitors that early man found grazing among the wet lowlands in Egypt. The distinguished ethnologist Dr. Carl Sauer believes that these animals were caught and kept ready at first only as sacrifices for the gods. Utility followed religion when the cattle began to breed in captivity. By the thirtieth century B.C., according to clear drawings dating from that time, the Egyptians had developed their domesticated herds into a long-horned and a hornless stock, and were using the animals for dragging crude plows, as well as for a source of milk and beef. The cattle of today's Watussi herdsmen wear the same lyre-shaped horns as are depicted on ancient Egyptian inscriptions. The inverted head of such an animal is believed to have inspired the letter A. Whatever the length of their horns and wherever they may be, cattle still require for healthy growth almost the same amount of water per pound as did their ancestors in the wetlands of Egypt.

Unlike the native antelopes of equatorial Africa, which can go for a week without a drink and then come to a waterhole cautiously by a well-worn narrow trail, the cattle of the Watussi and Masai tribes must have water every day or two. The animals are kept within a half day's driving distance of water while they forage for soft vegetation under the thorn scrub, which they ignore. In the interests of manageability and faster growth, man has bred fear out of his animals. As a result, they straggle to a waterhole from all directions, trampling the vegetation and crashing noisily through the bushes. Through clumsiness the cattle destroy more potential food than they eat. And, although the herdsmen drive their animals from the foraging area around one waterhole to the next as soon as the supply of edible plants or water gives out, the vegetation near each waterhole dies off farther and farther away. No longer do the native antelopes feel safe to approach what little water remains after the cattle are driven on. No longer does the basin draining into the waterhole act as a sponge for rain and dew, releasing it continuously into the central pond. Instead, the bare earth erodes into the waterhole, filling it with silt and hurrying the day when no cud-chewing animal will be able to find there a pool from which to drink.

Pound for pound, the cud chewers that are native to the semiarid high country of Africa require only about a twentieth as much water as do the domesticated cattle. The impalas, hartebeests, gnus, and elands, the giraffes and rhinos all manage with a minimum of moisture. In company with zebras, elephants, warthogs, and ostriches, or in family groups, or great herds of a single kind, each of these indigenous animals seeks its favorite food plants in its preferred habitat and overlaps surprisingly little with the others. Together this seething assortment of vegetarians prune with a minimum of trampling virtually every kind of plant from the shortest grasses to the thorny, flat-topped trees. Without a herdsboy to guide them, they move on when their particular kind of forage becomes harder to find. In this way, the mixed character of the thorn scrub is retained, whereas man's cattle progressively eliminate the softer kinds of vegetation and transform the country into one of prickly dwarf trees with thick bark and little effect in retarding erosion.

The black people who are now assuming new responsibilities in an emerging Africa need the wisdom of a Solomon to decide on actions that will preserve their little countries as places where people will be able to live. In today's freedom to change the rules from those imposed by colonial powers, they are tempted to gain immediate popularity among the

herdsmen tribes by opening all of the national parks
and wildlife reserves to unrestricted grazing. Repeal
of antipoaching laws would make available to their
people, who crave meat, the remaining herds of
wildlife until all were exterminated. Most of the
Africans regard wild animals only as fresh meat that
is benefiting none of them; or as competitors with
their cattle for forage and water; or as a mark of the
primitive past that should be obliterated in making
way for cities, automobiles, and television. A few,
fortunately, realize that nothing in their country can
attract the tourist dollars, pounds, reichsmarks and
new francs to the extent that wildlife can. Nothing
their land produces as a renewable resource provides
such a reliable income. As in America, economic
reasons sometimes support the arguments of the conservationist, particularly if long-term planning takes
precedence over expediency.

Now that the future of Africa's once-stupendous
herds of wildlife is in the balance, with native sentiment overwhelmingly in favor of obliterating it completely and forever, crash programs to study the
animals are in progress. From many of these has
come the idea that the wisest move would be a rapid
replacement of cattle raising by antelope raising.
In Rhodesia, a square mile of dry thorn scrub can be
made to carry 21,000 pounds of beef cattle, but not
without considerable erosion. In Albert National
Park, the same area of similar land supports 139,000
pounds of wild cud chewers without difficulty. The
largest of these native meat animals reach full size
in two to three years, and the smaller ones in one
year—much as deer do in America. By contrast,

domestic cattle need four years to reach marketable size while hunting for food in a land where the kind they need is virtually absent. From his personal investigations in Southern Rhodesia, and experience on the Henderson Ranch there, Dr. R. F. Dasmann of Humboldt State College in California has concluded that between ten and twenty times as much meat could be harvested from these semiarid lands if the domestic cattle, sheep, and goats were eliminated altogether.

Many of the antelopes have been found to take well to gentle herding. Eland (biggest of the antelopes) are now being bred on the ranch in Southern Rhodesia. Zebras have already been raised in captivity as a stunt; their meat is far superior to that of tired horses that are eaten in many parts of Europe, and occasionally at the Faculty Club of Harvard University. The impala, commonest of Africa's antelopes, would be an ideal addition to man's meat animals. Cape buffalo, like the eland, grow to larger size than a steer, but the need to harness these wild animals for draft purposes is likely to disappear in the New Africa. Surely antelope blood mixed with antelope milk, or zebra blood with zebra milk, would make just as good a Masai cocktail as the corresponding liquids from a cow.

Probably it would be harder to convince a Masai father that six majestic eland would be as good a price for his daughter as six skinny cows have been. No matter how handsome, the wild thing is rarely valued as highly as the tame. We recall a South African man who was deeply insulted, and ready to call off his own wedding to an English girl at her home near London, all because the church was decorated with calla lilies. He knew them only as weeds in disused fields, from which their roots are sometimes dug as food for pigs. They have almost no commercial value. In South Africa, the small children sometimes gather an armful of calla lilies in innocent delight, just as little girls in America occasionally bring home a big bouquet of dandelions and hawkweeds. No matter how beautiful these wild flowers might be, no bride would choose to carry them on her trip to the altar. Her bouquet, and the decorations in the church, must come from a florist. Like hothouse flowers, the cattle in equatorial Africa cost more—particularly in water. Actually, they are capital assets. But unlike money or land that brings a return when managed wisely, the domesticated herds are a liability, destroying the land because they demand more water than the climate allows.

The recommendation that domesticated cattle be replaced as a source of milk, meat, hides, and other useful products in equatorial Africa sounds more convincing in America than on the Dark Continent. The same shoe can pinch our feet as well. In western Texas and many another part of our semiarid Southwest, any land too poor for plant crops and too remote to irrigate is "cow country." To fit this definition it must support at least one cow to the section (one square mile). When the cattle that survive reach full size, horsemen round them up by riding through the chaparral of sagebrush, greasewood, cactus, and mesquite. Sometimes the cowhands take off time to hunt the small herds of fleet-footed pronghorn antelopes that are native to the same countryside.

Rarely do the pronghorns visit the watering places that must be prepared for cattle. Yet a full-grown buck at 125 pounds or a doe at 90 is fat and sleek, whereas the cattle that are to be shipped soon to centers for "finishing" by feeding on corn and other grain are lean to the point of being scrawny. Right here at home we could probably replace all domestic animals on the arid western ranges with herds of pronghorns and harvest these on a commercial scale. They would be an asset to perpetuate into the future, providing more than a target for a sportsman's gun. Almost certainly the same section that now yields a few cows each year would produce ten times as much meat in pronghorn form. It is finished meat, requiring no additional feeding to marble it with fat. That it comes in smaller pieces should not be as important as the fact that it takes less water and makes thriftier use of arid lands.

If it were not for custom, the same principle might be extended in America in several areas. In the East and among the mountains of the West, where cattle and sheep feed between the outcropping boulders of pasture land, the native shrubs and seedling trees spring up quickly if allowed to do so. This is just the type of browse that deer enjoy; we could harvest more venison by raising deer on these lands than by striving so hard for beef and lamb. In the swampy northern forests of spruce, a great many more moose could be produced if the undertaking rated half the care now given to growing pulpwood.

Even the desert rodents, and the prairie dogs and ground squirrels of less arid land should not be overlooked. They transform the native plants into meat with less expenditure of water than any meat animal man raises. Surely it would take no more explanation in introducing a foreign visitor to a hot dog to assure him that the meat was ground squirrel than that it was beef. Some of our friends who have sampled groundhog insist that they enjoy it as much as most meats from the butchershop.

Currently in Australia a similar change in policy might be tried. At present the kangaroos are being slaughtered in tremendous numbers, with the approval of the ranchers, who see a chance to raise more beef and mutton if their cud chewers have fewer kangaroos for competition. The makers of pet food roam the "out-back" with rifles and refrigerator trucks, and efficiently transform kangaroo meat into tidbits for dogs and cats. The hides provide an extra profit as long as a market remains for the leather. Privately, Australians tell us that there is nothing wrong with a kangaburger, and that steaks or roasts cut by a skillful butcher from a two-hundred pound gray kangaroo are just as good as those from a thousand-pound steer. Kangaroos are far better fitted to live in the Australian bush than are man's cattle. For sustained yield of meat useful to man—and to his carnivorous pets, if he insists, while millions of people remain malnourished for want of protein from animal sources—kangaroos might make much more efficient use of Australia's limited resources in fresh water than any rancher's herds and flocks.

From a thoughtful and open-minded review of the wild plants and native animals living in the drier parts of the whole world, ingenious man could compile a new list of potential foods. Each item in his list would bear a price tag, as well as an inventory of the nourishing ingredients it offered. The price would be in water, showing clearly how much moisture would be required from the total bounty available to man, if the new food were raised in quantity, allowing some old-time crop plant or animal to be replaced.

It is unreasonable to assume that all of the plants and animals in the world that can offer almost perfect foods were discovered by early man. We have no cause to credit our remote ancestors with either consistently special luck or a premonition of gain beyond that to be seen today among people living at a subsistence level. Luck surely has played a part, for the Spanish conquerors could not have known that the marble-sized potatoes they took home as curiosities from the lofty land of the Incas in South America would lead to the mealy marvels for which Idaho and Maine are famous. In the two-inch heads of teosinte maize grown by the Indians from Chile to Canada there is little hint of the prize ears of hybrid corn that are the pride of Kansas. Yet these plants, like the other crops and the domesticated animals, have changed over the centuries through selective breeding, becoming the foods we prize today.

None of the crops raised in quantity in the modern world is new. Almost all of them were being cultivated to the best of man's ability two thousand years ago. In many cases, they were chosen because they matched the needs of the time for ease in transport and storage as much as for nutrition. Cereals could be dried and hoarded indefinitely, so long as rodents and insects were excluded. Tractable beasts from adjacent wetlands became the domesticated animals as much because their milk and meat would keep without refrigeration while the animals were alive in pens as for any special liking for their products.

Ingenious man now boasts that he can turn into something tasty, salable, and free of special hazards to health virtually everything in a pig, a steer, or a sheep. He can capture the nourishment and most of the flavor of a potato, an onion, a glass of milk, or a cup of coffee, then package it in foil or can or jar. All that is needed to make it food again is an instant— and WATER. If this same ingenuity is turned to getting more food without added water, the human species will once more have converted a dangerous dependence upon a limited resource into a new freedom.

14

THE GENIUS OF WATER

OLD-TIMERS recalled droughts worse than this year's, but not since 1930. The fire marshal closed the woods to everyone. Each lookout tower atop a hill or mountain was manned from dawn to dusk. Fire trucks, their sirens shrilling, rushed to the site of any rising column of smoke that could not be accounted for. Volunteers from the villages patrolled all the back roads every night, ready to summon aid at the first sign of flames. City folk turned quickly to the weather column of the newspaper, seeking a forecast of rain. They found, instead, reports on how low the water level stood in every reservoir. And warnings: there might not be enough water to quench a major fire.

Rarely had the fall colors reached such magnificence in the Northeast. Yet New Englanders were almost too apprehensive of a disastrous conflagration to appreciate their autumn splendor. At the height of the season, we visited some friends in eastern Vermont. Never before had the view seemed so spectacular from their house on the crest of a ridge. They urged us to stay. "I do hope, though, that you've had baths recently," our hostess added with true Yankee

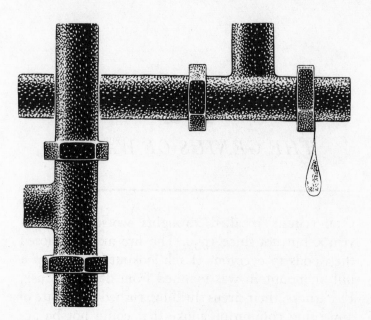

candor. "Our well is completely dry, and we've been hauling water from the valley for nearly two months now. It's weeks since I've had more than a sponge bath myself. But there's a pitcher of water in the bathroom, and more downstairs in the kitchen. Just don't use the toilet. It's like the old days, with no indoor plumbing."

We thought of the summer cottage in northern Ontario, before electricity became available. Water for drinking and cooking came from a covered spring in the sheep pasture on the other side of the hill. Each day we hauled it two pailfuls at a time, and sometimes had trouble with the full-grown ewe that had once been a pet lamb and still wanted to show affection by butting against our legs. For washing and for boiling eggs we fetched water in different pails from the lake, up seventy irregular steps that seemed to be two hundred. ("No, Lorus, you can't cook the eggs in the teakettle!") We used as little water as we could, but never did decide which type of bath left us cleaner: a sponge bath with a basin of warmed water from the big pot on the back of the wood stove; or a really quick one at the edge of the lake in the early morning before anyone would notice, when the water felt icy and the air still colder. Laundry, of course, was done at the boat dock, or carried back unwashed to the city, where piped water and washing machine made the task so much easier.

Our thoughts shifted to the cool water that ran reliably from the faucets in the city. When we were children it was left running constantly in the kitchen sink during hot weather, to spare us the annoyance of waiting to draw off the warmed water in the pipes before enjoying a cooling drink. In Toronto, until we had an electric refrigerator, the same cool water filled one laundry tub in the basement for most of the summer. Quietly it escaped from the overflow at the top, vanishing into the drain at the same rate as it was replaced by a small stream from the open faucet. Quart bottles of fresh milk, tethered to the faucets by cords, dangled into the water, where the milk stayed sweet for about the same number of days as though it had been standing in a cool springhouse on a farm. At the surface of the cool water filling the tub cucumbers often bobbed. They stayed crisp far better than in any modern refrigerator.

That this was wasting water never entered our heads. After all, the water came from Lake Ontario,

and ran back to it again through sewers. It couldn't
cost much to pump the little we used rather than
buy an icebox and ice. Milk didn't have to be *ice* cold.

In most countries where water flows freely at the
turn of a valve, the generous use of water and careless waste have been encouraged by public policy.
For more than a century, water commissions have
pretended that furnishing plenty of water is cheaper
than providing a modest amount. In the early days
of municipal systems, promotional tricks of this kind
seemed necessary. People with backyard wells and
pit privies needed considerable convincing that, for
almost no cost, they could have an unlimited amount
of water if only they would have their houses con-
nected to the mains and sewers.

Over the years, as the quantity of fresh water
available per person has decreased progressively, no
fundamental change has been made in this system of
pricing. The person who uses a great deal of water
still expects to pay a much lower average cost per
gallon than the man who is economical with it. In
Karachi, Pakistan, and Tel Aviv, Israel—both of
them expanding in an arid land, the water bill is
calculated according to the assessed value of the
property. The owner of a large estate is persuaded
to waste water, for he must pay for it anyway.

The situation is scarcely different in our two
largest cities. Neither New York nor Chicago has yet
made more than a token attempt to install water
meters, although a whole series of investigations by
experts have pointed out the gain that would follow.
Both cities continue to "consume" an average of
about 73 gallons *more* per day per person than cities

with meters throughout; this is a fair measure of the wasted water. At present, a flat rate of $13 is charged any New Yorker who owns a building more than 18 and less than 20 feet wide, and no more than five stories high, if he has only one bathtub; extra bathtubs incur an additional $4.50 annually. Each restaurant pays $12 a year for the huge amounts that go through the dishwashers and into the preparation of foods, or onto the tables. If the premises are air-conditioned, an extra charge of $7.50 annually is made for an installation using between a half and one gallon of water per minute; this is a real bargain —a thousand gallons for 1¾ cents.

Ever since July, 1842, when New York City took over from The Manhattan Company the responsibility for keeping residents and industries there supplied with water, each recommendation in favor of water meters has been ignored or followed only half-heartedly. By 1900, almost a third of New York's water actually went through meters, which made it worthwhile to turn off faucets and repair leaks. Since then the percentage of meters has fallen off, despite a 1900 report to The Merchants' Association by J. J. R. Croes and Foster Crowell urging more meters and less building of dams. These two investigators concluded that the 117 gallons per person per day then used in New York could be accounted for by 62 gallons wasted, 30 actually used by householders and unmetered businesses, 20 by factories and other metered organizations, and 5 by the city in washing streets, putting out fires and operating public drinking fountains. The same recommendation came from the Bureau of the Budget in 1948 to

Mayor William O'Dwyer, with an estimate that 220 million gallons per day would be saved from waste if meters were installed, and another $9 million in revenues collected for the water sold on a volume basis.

To provide New York's five boroughs with so much water to use and waste, the commissioners have relied on an authority granted to the city in May, 1834. It allows them to condemn property in adjacent areas upstate wherever they deem it necessary, to collect and impound water behind special dams. The water commissioners could have made use of the Hudson River, above its salty estuary where it flows past the city. Poughkeepsie has found feasible the purification of Hudson River water to domestic standards. Instead, the commissioners have now spent about a billion dollars to flood seventeen valleys. The money has paid for land, dams, and aqueducts in which to bring home the water. Counting the new Cannonsville Reservoir, now under construction, the area flooded comes to about 150 square miles, which is almost half as much as the total of all land within the city limits.

The proponents of thrift have not given up. As recently as 1960, a team of investigators sponsored by the RAND Corporation of Santa Monica concluded that neither New York City nor southern California had any present need for new water facilities. The aqueduct from Cannonsville alone is costing twice as much as would the installation of water meters throughout New York City at the present price of $35 each. Each year, they stated, the city is throwing away half as much water as the Cannonsville Reservoir can deliver, just by failing to stop leakage from its mains. No one seriously questions these calculations. Yet the balance of decision remains tilted toward waste.

If people paid for water according to the amount taken, as they do for fuel oil or gasoline or milk, the direct costs would almost certainly rise. But the cost of getting water for them to use or waste could also be divided realistically. At 180 gallons per person per day, five people use an acre-foot in a year, at a wholesale cost of about $78 from Cannonsville. Landlords see themselves going bankrupt if charged at this rate, unless each apartment has its own meter. This is not impossible, especially since New York City has made a practice of making the users with meters pay for the meters upon installation. Taxpayers doubt, however, that the revenues from sale of water by meters would be used to lower taxes; new undertakings might easily absorb it.

Installation of water meters would bring no glory to the Department of Buildings, which is most directly concerned with waste; or to the Department of Water Supply, Gas and Electricity, which maintains the water mains and sewers; or to the Bureau of the Budget, which divides the city's revenues among its multiple demands; or to the three commissioners on the Board of Water Supply. A water commissioner appears a greater hero, saving a city from thirst, by announcing the completion of a new dam, reservoir, and aqueduct than by stating that no new construction will be needed because New Yorkers with meters will buy only half as much water as they have been consuming unmetered.

If New Yorkers think at all about the reservoirs upstate, they regard them as a vast system of lakes they have paid to establish. When they see in the newspaper a brief mention that the grubbing contractors have now cleared away all encumbrances from the site of the new Cannonsville Reservoir, they rarely realize that "encumbrances" are more than roads, power poles, and trees. The unspecified items include people, homes, churches, cemeteries, stores, cows, and crops of many kinds. Already the 150 square miles of impounded waters for New York City have drowned the three areas of highest milk production in the whole state. Unlike an office clerk or an apartment dweller, who can move from one building to another without much loss, the dairymen and farmers cannot use the money they get for their expropriated land to buy the equivalent somewhere else. They are not paid for the climate that made their agricultural operations a success, or for the care they gave the topsoil to make it yield at peak production into perpetuity. Nothing comparable close to a city market is available at the price they receive.

Over the whole United States, similar encumbrances have been removed and valuable areas destroyed to benefit many people at the expense of fewer. Between 1940 and 1960, reservoirs flooded 3,130 additional square miles, decreasing by that amount the land area tallied by the Census Bureau. When compared to the 2,975,000 square miles in the contiguous states in 1940, the loss seems trivial: a tenth of 1 percent in two decades. Yet we cannot overlook those encumbrances, or answer the nagging question: How much impoundment was really necessary. At the Federal and State level, just as much glory is attached to constructing a huge dam and just as little to saving water by less expensive means.

Another puff to status, costing a great deal of water, impressed us first on a blazing afternoon we had spent crossing the Nevada desert. Suddenly, around a curve in the road, we saw on a hillside ahead a patch of brilliant green. After all the tans, reddish browns, and pastel gray-greens of the arid landscape through which we had been passing, it was unbelievable. At last our car brought us close enough to identify neat lawns that would have done credit to a Connecticut estate with forty-five inches of rain a year and a humid breeze off the ocean all night every night. Those lawns, where the annual rainfall averages less than five inches, were the pride of nearly thirty thousand people in Boulder City, who watered them regularly and at low cost from a municipal supply piped out of Lake Mead.

With cheap electricity from the turbines in nearby Hoover Dam, most of the houses, offices, and shops in Boulder City are delightfully air-conditioned. The lawns and lawn sprinklers cool the outdoor air, where few people are. Mostly the green improves appearance, conferring on this amazing oasis in the midst of the desert the token of respectability recognized in New England. Grass matches the buildings, which show so little western influence that an Easterner feels right at home. Not many houses in this community, which is made possible only by the dammed waters of the Colorado River, have a flagstone patio and border vegetation in place of a lawn. Yet this western alternative in architecture conserves moisture and still provides wonderful relief from the bare desert stretching away on all sides.

At the national and state level, each new impoundment of water costs more than the one before. Not only are costs of labor rising, but we are fighting the law of diminishing returns. Already all of the easy projects have been put into operation. Yet the Army Corps of Engineers and the Bureau of Reclamation follow no master plan with a finite end. Construction goes on, usually to the delight of congressmen. If a group of them were challenged, some scholar might quote Longinus, the Greek philosopher and critic who died in A.D. 273: "Which is the better . . . grandeur with a few flaws or mediocrity that is impeccable?" Few would fail to identify wasted water as a flaw.

During the dry months of 1963, a constant stream of statistics appeared, showing how the drought in the Northeast was progressing. New talk of preventing waste raised hopes that something worthwhile would be done. Suggestions that still more reservoirs be built found about equal support. The important question was whether 1964 would be a third year in succession with less than normal rainfall. New York City's reservoirs began 1962 at capacity, but after the normal drawdown of summer were restored to only the 86 percent level. By October, 1963, they held enough for just 117 days at the average rate of withdrawal. If another meager amount of precipitation came during the following autumn, winter, and spring, New York might be out of water by the end of the 1964 summer. No help could be expected from the new Cannonsville reservoir before 1965—

and then not until precipitation filled it. Yet, to collect water for the city, the reservoirs actually in operation during 1963 took virtually every drop that fell on an area forty times the size of Manhattan. When filled to capacity, they hold enough water to inundate that island borough to a depth of 110 feet.

We wondered how much work a gallon of water should do as it travels from the reservoir through the conduits, out of a faucet, down a drain, and on toward the sewer and sea. The 1.2 billion gallons a day that follow this route through some 5,800 miles of water mains in New York City alone should accomplish a tremendous amount. A hundred and seventy-three gallons per person per day is a lot for New Yorkers to take for their sole benefit, away from ducks, deer, fishes, and other types of life over such a large area. Since we take their lives when we take away their water, we can scarcely justify depriving them of the vital liquid so that we can waste it.

In the spring of 1964, the post offices in New York cancelled mail with the words SAVE WATER. The slogan may have stimulated an appreciation for the liquid that still came so abundantly in municipal supplies, that made life easier for millions of citizens. We treasure more readily the solid signs of civilization in cities, and tend to overlook the flowing water without which we cannot enjoy the rest.

Very occasionally, someone decides to show in a tangible way his gratitude for the blessings that water brings. Rarely can he find the artistic means to express his wishes. August von Kreling, a young German sculptor, had such an idea in 1840. He drew up detailed plans for the symbolic statuary he would like to see combined into a splendid fountain, one dedicated to the "genius of water." He took his design to Colonel Ferdinand von Miller, director of the Royal Bavarian Foundry. But no funds were raised to pay for the work. The plans gathered dust until 1857, when Henry Probasco of Cincinnati visited the foundry in search of just such a design. The successful hardware merchant from Ohio promptly commissioned the statues to be cast in bronze. In 1871 they were unveiled as the centerpiece of Fountain Square, and formally donated to the City of Cincinnati in the name of Probasco's brother-in-law and business partner, Tyler Davidson.

Visited annually by thousands of people, the historic fountain still stands, dominated by a woman's figure of heroic size. She is the "Genius of Water," from the tips of whose fingers on outstretched arms a steady rain descends. To the north, it falls on a man's figure depicted with his last bucket empty, trying to quench the flames on his burning housetop. To the south, it reaches a farmer beside his plow and vine, praying for water to save his crops. To the east, a mother leads her young son to bathe. To the west, a daughter brings a cup of water to her aged father. Great plaques on the central pedestal show in bold relief man's use of water in shipping, for fisheries, for water power, and for grinding grain. Niches in the corners of the column enhance charming figures of smaller size: a boy putting on his skates, a laughing girl twisting a necklace of pearls around her neck and gazing at her reflection in a pool below, a boy with a lobster freshly taken from his net, a little girl with a seashell at her ear. On outlying pedestals around the

broad basin at the foot of the column, still other
bronze figures give a feeling of space to the whole
group. A fine curtain of water rises into the air from
the rim of the basin behind them; at night they are
silhouetted against the illuminated jets and sculp-
tures of the central column.

To encounter this refreshing group of statuary
amid the tall buildings of the Fifth Street Esplanade
is to enjoy a moment of discovery. Walking around
and examining them from every angle, we marveled
at the realism that has been captured in the polished
metal. To how many people have August von
Kreling and Henry Probasco brought a new appreciation for the water that makes civilization possible?
In almost a century, the number of passersby is in-
calculable, as untallied as the volume of water flowing down the Ohio River a few city blocks away. In
those years, the traffic on Fifth Street has changed
from horse-drawn vehicles and men in tall top hats
to one-way passage of sleek automobiles and side-
walks full of people in modern garb. The river flows
at new levels, maintained by great dams, and serves
as a waterway for far-different types of boats and
barges. But the uses of water in the metropolis increase more than they change in kind. If Tyler
Davidson could return and admire the fountain erec-
ted in his honor, he would recognize in the American
scene today the continued dependence of people and
all life on water. To be careful with water is to conserve life itself.

15

WATER OVER THE DAM

THROUGH yesterday and all last night, the blessed rain came down, sometimes scarcely more than a caressing mist, oftener a pelting torrent. The grass that had grown crisp and brown from four weeks without more than a morning film of dew softened and straightened as though ready to grow again. An inch of rain came in less than twenty-four hours—a ten-day supply at the rate we have learned to expect.

In celebration, we sipped a cup of coffee soon after dawn and then took a pre-breakfast stroll down to the old dam. Over it an inch of water curved like liquid satin, then crashed on the boulders below with a cheery roar we had welcomed from the farthest side of the broad millpond. Enough spray caught in the wind to enrich the air near the dam with a fresh bouquet, one that plucked from our minds the memories of other waterfalls. It is the fragrance of the great horseshoe that thunders at Niagara, and of the palm-fringed canyon rim opposite Victoria Falls on the broad Zambezi.

The song and scent of water where our little Oyster River descends its last ten feet to join the tides in the long estuary and Great Bay remind us of thousands

239

of natural waterfalls throughout the world. But, as in all of these places where a river rushes over a rim to drop precipitously, the water we hear and smell caresses only the esthetic sense. Its energy is wasted, converted to sound and heat—including the hidden calories that turn some of the liquid to invisible vapor. It helps no living thing any more than does the reflection we admire in the smooth waters of the millpond, mirroring the trees around the shore and the white steeple of the church upon the hill beyond.

For fifty years no one has regulated the metal door to the millrace at the end of the old dam. The mill went out of business, fell into disrepair, and was torn down, largely because the water power grew too intermittent, too undependable. Too often the level of the millpond fell below the cement lip of the dam, and any prolonged use of water would have drained the reservoir.

Even in its best days, the mill beside the dam we know so well was limited by the small size of the Oyster River. Yet it is representative also of the big rivers of the world. As the outstanding geographer Dr. Gilbert F. White of the University of Chicago pointed out to an Arizona audience in 1960, "Great basins such as the Nile and the Tigris-Euphrates still discharge 40 percent or more of their mean flows without economic return. . . . Paradoxical as it may seem, in the arid zone large volumes of water annually evaporate from playas or flow into the sea without having served human needs." In some cases, on the sites where centers of ancient culture stood, ignorance and lack of capital combine today to keep people impoverished, parched, and malnourished while the power of a great river goes to waste close by. Often the former civilization flourished because of the river, and fell when the water that was taken for granted slipped away.

"Water over the dam" represents all the opportunities in life that are missed because they are not grasped in time. Certainly the particular molecules that overflow the brink and plunge to lower levels can never be recalled. But others take their place, as long as the river runs. The fresh water that condenses on the high peaks and flows to the sea seldom vanishes without leaving hope behind.

All over the world today, some men are looking for ways to benefit from hindsight. They seek to reduce the amount of water that goes over dams, making more available to the growing needs of human populations. Other men seem confident in alternatives. So, the legend tells, was Belshazzar, the king of Babylon, who disbelieved Daniel's interpretation of the mystic writing on the wall: MENE, MENE, TEKEL, UPHARSIN. He continued to feast with a thousand of his lords, secure in a mountain of stored food. It would last for many months of siege, while Darius with his Medes and Persians surrounded the metropolis outside the walls. But for weeks the soldiers of Darius had been digging a great ditch around the city. When it was finished, Darius used it to divert the Euphrates upon which Babylon depended for water. Realizing that they could not hold out for even a week, his own Chaldeans slew Belshazzar while he feasted. They opened the gates to Darius, whose simple weapon was human thirst.

Long before Darius' time, men showed ingenuity

with water. All over the world they discovered in-
dependently how to plant their row crops in a continuous series of narrow terraces on every hillside.
Between rows the distance is too small and the furrow
too deep for the water from any one hard rain ever
to overflow. Instead, it remains as a narrow pond a
few inches wide and many feet long. Gradually the
moisture sinks into the soil close to the roots; the rest
evaporates in the sun and wind.

We marvel that farmers on all sloping land did not
learn the trick of terracing to capture moisture and
stop erosion. Every child seems to know how. At the
roadsides in New England, youngsters sometimes
build dams of mud and sand, busy as beavers in the
ditch or gutter, stopping the erosive currents that
they find gurgling along. We have watched the boys
and girls with a Mayan heritage doing the same thing
on the steep slopes of old volcanoes in the highlands
of Guatemala. During the rain or immediately afterward they went splashing happily, digging with their
small hands to rebuild any earthern ridge that showed signs of weakening. How much, we wondered,
was play and how much was work for the good of the
family's terraced crops?

In the Near East during ancient times, the people
grew more expert at capturing the intermittent rain.
Out of the fields they moved the stones, into long
rows that followed the contours. They banked the
soil until each stone wall could be seen only from
down slope. There the stones served as the lips of
dams a foot or two in height, resisting erosion whenever the rain fell too rapidly to sink into the flat cultivated field which extended to the next stone wall up-

hill. In this simple way the farmers held the scanty supply of water in the soil as though it were a savings bank. Their crops drew moisture reliably far into the dry season. But under the repeated wars that swept back and forth, this dry-land farming could not last. Too many generals believed in a scorched-earth policy. Like the Romans who conquered Carthage, they destroyed the land they took by smashing anything that could hold water, and often by spreading salt on the fields as well.

Today these parts of the Near East remain scorched by the sun. The few people living there neither know nor care to rebuild the stone walls and the soil to capture the rain. Instead all of the moisture from springtime rushes through gaps in the stones as a muddy flood that is soon gone, without helping any living thing.

Millions of people now benefit by delaying the downward flow of moisture from the mountains to the sea. From each step in the long stair of water they expect to gain. Among the various ways in which they secure this profit, the differences match chiefly the amount of rainfall to be managed or the cost of laborers who have the skill needed to handle the local situation. In the Philippines, under an annual rainfall of eighty inches, all members of a family tend the rims of their own paddy fields. For months, every patch of rice remains a shallow pond from which water evaporates more slowly than it accumulates from rains. The excess is drained away with care, to prevent erosion. In Iowa, the corn farmer is equally intent on capturing all of his thirty inches of annual rain and snow, on letting none overflow the ridge between two furrows and carry off his soil. He guides a powerful tractor and a giant plow around the contours of a rolling cornfield that may be a mile across, adhering closely to a pattern laid out for him by a surveying team armed with a theodolite and a stadia rod.

Near Lubbock, Texas, where the annual rainfall is only about twenty-one inches, another man drives his snorting bulldozer to throw up the earth from a broad band of sloping land. He too follows the contours, trying a new version of the ancient system for trapping water. His product is a narrow, level reservoir, called a contour bench, rimmed on the downhill side by a high ridge of earth. Between one bench with its ridge and the next is a zone of untouched slope, which is both the place for crops and also a watershed. From it after any one rain, no more water must drain off than will cover his contour bench to a depth of six inches. This water is to seep into the soil of the watershed below, and increase the yield of the crop on the slope between one rain and the next. If the crop is cotton, the yield may be a fourth more than before he built his water traps. In a single year he earns enough to pay the entire costs of surveying and bulldozing the bench terraces, even though these exceed $11,400 a square mile. Thereafter, his gain is all profit.

Where the rainfall is still less, it must be collected from a tremendous area to be helpful to man. The task ceases to be one that a family or a man and machine can handle. It becomes a statewide or a Federal project to transform a whole river basin into a stairway of managed water. Although far more planning, cooperation, and expense are called for, more people are served. A river is a community possession, and valuable in many enterprises. So mixed are the benefits it offers that the gains about which little is heard may outweigh the cost of restraining its water. They often overbalance the inconvenience to a few people, which sometimes gets so much publicity.

Among the most famous of these giant projects to save water from going over the dam is the one managed by the Tennessee Valley Authority. So many conflicting statements have been published about it that we decided to visit the area and see what is there. We knew that when Congress created this corporation, the Tennessee River had only one dam. It provided electric power in the northwest corner of Alabama to the munitions and fertilizer factories at nearby Muscle Shoals. For much of the year then, the Tennessee was not navigable. Almost every spring its rushing floodwaters joined those from the Ohio River at Paducah, Kentucky, and roared onward into the Mississippi, helping increase the havoc all the way to New Orleans. Along the Tennessee lived some of the nation's poorest people, on eroded hillside farms with almost none of the conveniences of modern times. Only the valley bottomland produced reliable crops. Wild was the outcry after 1933 when the new project began inundating all of this valuable area.

Today, at a cost of slightly more than $2 billion, the TVA has twenty-five dams of its own and controls the flow of water through six more, which were built by the Aluminum Corporation of America. Resembling a series of huge cement-sided bathtubs, each draining into the next, the reservoirs behind the dams have a combined capacity sufficient to hold all of the spring runoff. It is used to stop water from the Tennessee going into the Ohio and Mississippi whenever the levels of these rivers rise and threaten to cause trouble. Complete stoppage does not interfere with navigation on the many lakes of the TVA, or through the locks that bypass the barriers. Now 650 miles of river are used by industrial barge lines and by private pleasure craft. For much of the year, the small boats of fishermen dot the lakes, transforming an area with essentially no recreational appeal into one of the most popular in the country. The fishermen really catch fish.

For safeguarding the democratic way of life at the beginning of World War II, the TVA fulfilled undreamed dreams. Within a few months, its vast resources of hydroelectric power were converted from peaceful to military use. By the end of the Korean War, additional demands for electricity in government-owned atomic plants far exceeded the power available from water going through the turbines at the dams. Now the TVA produces twice as much electricity in coal-burning steam plants as it does by water power, and is the nation's largest consumer of coal. But the unsung gains once more rise high, because electricity is available inexpensively for the people along the river's tortuous path. It has infused new ambitions, given return for effort, and transformed a sadly depressed area into one of relative prosperity. People work to earn radios and television sets, and to keep up with the outside world from which they formerly stayed apart. To improve the soil they buy fertilizer and machines, and see good crops grow where almost nothing of value matured before. The soil, so carefully tended, stays on the land and grows richer year by year instead of eroding into a muddy river. These people, more than most, know the revolution in living that can come in thirty years when water is stopped from flowing over the dam.

Along the Tennessee, neither the people nor their crops have any cause to be thirsty, for between fifty and fifty-five inches of rain fall each year on the slopes and lakes that drain this part of the country. No one worries about evaporation of water from the reservoirs behind the dams, or how to apportion the generous flow of the river among cities, industries, fishermen, and farmers. These are real problems, however, along the Colorado River, which is twice as long as the Tennessee but even at flood season contains less than half as much water. For most of its length, the Colorado is out of place—flowing through a desert where the annual rainfall varies between five and twenty inches and the dry air is usually warm enough to absorb all of its water.

Few rivers in the world are as controlled and parsimoniously rationed as the Colorado. Few lose as much water as they flow along. Indeed, the challenge presented by this river in the desert is not the water that overflows the dams but the moisture that vanishes before reaching the barriers. Efforts to use more of the Colorado's water are likely to set a pattern throughout the world, as people everywhere try to gain more from the limited supply of moisture that is fresh enough to drink or to use for irrigation.

Ever since the Colorado filled Lake Mead behind Hoover Dam, which was built in 1936 along the border between Arizona and Nevada, the Arizonans have dreamed of using the moisture that evaporates constantly from the lake surface. In the course of a year, this amounts to between 5½ and 7½ inches of water over the entire 247 square miles. It is more than as much water as flows in all Arizona rivers other than the Colorado. Additional reservoirs and stock ponds in the state shrink at the same pace by evaporation, bringing the total lost into the air from open water to between 165 and 185 billion gallons annually. Lake Mead—largest man-made reservoir in America—holds only about 58 times this total when filled to the brim. If Arizonans could prevent the evaporation from open water, they would have twice as much of the precious liquid to use as they do now.

Great as this benefit would be, it could not now justify the cost of a truly water-tight roof over Lake Mead or any other large reservoir, hiding the impoundment from the sun and dry air. So extreme a measure would save water. But it would also end the use of these lakes for swimming and waterskiing, boating and fishing. In the United States, these recreational values far exceed the importance of any crops that could be grown with the extra moisture. Calculations about alternative uses for the water that evaporates do not yet seem realistic. They show that 25 million acre-feet escape from the nation's reservoirs, that this much water would irrigate eight million acres, where crops could be raised to feed at least 16 million people. At present, this number of customers have not come forward with money of their own to spend on the food we might produce if we invested in maximum thrift with our water.

A compromise is being sought through chemistry, one that will save from 30 to 50 percent of the water that now evaporates, without decreasing the purity of the water or its suitability for fishes, people, and boats. Already the chemists have tried floating a film of insoluble alcohols on stock ponds in Oklahoma and Australia; evaporation is reduced by nearly 10 percent, which pays for the cost of the materials. But the thin layer, only one or two molecules thick, is broken easily by boats or swimmers, and does not mend itself quickly. A steady wind can drive it to one shore. Moreover, if as much as half of a pond or lake is coated, the fishes and other aquatic life die, fouling the water. Fortunately, improvements seem within reach. In May, 1963, at the annual meeting of the American Water Works Association in Kansas City, the conferees were told that they might expect soon to be able to spread on their reservoirs a more lasting, harmless, tasteless film costing only a few cents for each thousand gallons of water saved.

The ingenious chemists are trying also to help the individual farmers, for whom the equivalent of water over the dam is more than half of the total that enters their fields. Under the best circumstances, water evaporates at an astonishing rate from the foliage of growing plants. With some of the new chemical sprays applied to the upper surfaces of all leaves, the water loss is reduced by 50 percent with only a 25 percent decrease in the productivity of the crop. Even this compromise may be worthwhile where water is expensive and the sale value of the product is high.

In the irrigated valleys of the Southwest, the farmers and truck gardeners buy the water they need from the supply canals, lead it into furrows between the crop plants, and then see much of it vanish by evaporation, leaving salt crystals on the soil. Even when no water is allowed to stand exposed in the field, at least half of the moisture that disappears into dry air has never reached a plant; it rises from the bare ground between the rows. Weeds aggravate the situation, and also send roots in among those of the crop plant, where they compete for water.

When polyethylene plastic became available in long thin black strips about a foot in width, some gardeners tried tacking down the material between the rows of crops. It stopped evaporation there, prevented weeds from growing, and still left a place for any rain that chanced along to reach the crops. But it was expensive to keep in place, and very much in the way. The strips occupied exactly those avenues between the crops down which irrigation water had to flow as needed, and where the wheels of implements rolled when the crops were being tended.

Cotton farmers, in particular, saw no hope in using strips of plastic film to save water. Then, in 1963, a new machine came on the market. It laid out the polyethylene from a roll, tacked it down, and put it between the irrigation avenues (or the wheel tracks) —right where the crop was to grow. At regular intervals the machine punched through the plastic and inserted in each hole a slug of vermiculite (exploded mica) containing a cotton seed and a specific amount each of a suitable fertilizer, fungicide, and insecticide. In this new location, the plastic film captures solar energy and warms the soil. It conserves water in the immediate vicinity of the seed and of the plant that grows from it. It prevents weeds from growing near the crop. Cotton raised in this way matures as much as a month early, and the picking machine can easily be modified to gather up the plastic film into a roll for burning. When used with muskmelons, squash, or tomatoes, the yield from the crop is about double.

When we wishfully consider the water that escapes by evaporation and dream of uses for it—if only we can keep it in the liquid state—we tend to forget that we are thinking of pure water. By contrast, the remainder after evaporation contains all of the dissolved salts. Whenever the dry air is allowed to absorb half of the water the river brings, it doubles the concentration of solutes in the remainder. Some rice farmers, who irrigate the broad flood plains near the mouth of a big river, can buy only water that already contains 250 parts of salt per million. By the time half of this water evaporates from the amount required to irrigate a crop for a whole season, a ton of salt has been added to each acre. To flush it out, before starting a new crop, they must buy more water, and hurry the solution back to the river— containing still more salt.

In its early stages of growth, a rice plant is sensitive to salt. If given water containing 600 parts per million, the rate of yield shrinks by about 25 percent; at 1,300 parts per million, the crop is 70 percent less than when given water with only 250 parts per million. The quality of the rice suffers too. And if the salt is allowed to accumulate, the soil itself becomes sticky, compact, and unable to absorb as much water. These changes in the land show why, in arid areas, irrigated fields can seldom continue to produce a crop for decade after decade. In many parts of the world, including both America and the Near East, the rate at which new irrigation schemes are put in operation at huge cost is matched fairly well by the rate at which old irrigated land must be quietly abandoned—too salty for further use until the climate changes and brings more rain. In the once-rich delta of the Nile, as in the great Indus Valley of Pakistan, fertility is fading fast because of salts left by prolonged irrigation.

The water in a river is just as lost to man as though it had gone over the dam and out to sea when the concentration of dissolved materials in it rises above what his crop plants and domesticated animals will tolerate. The few native kinds of plants that will survive on salt-encrusted soil get a quick start in a brief rainy season, and then draw water from deep in the earth. These plants are virtually all in the whole world that evolution has been able to provide with suitable adaptations in millions of years. Where the concentration of salts in the soil and ground water is high, even they are unable to grow.

Willows, tall cottonwoods, tamarisk, and greasewood thrive where little else does, if there is water no more than fifteen feet below the surface. Saltgrass forms a lush meadow only where a well that is dug seven feet deep will reach water. But it takes a lot of digging to outreach a leafless, tree-sized green mesquite. Many of these trees extend roots down to forty feet, and some to as deep as one hundred. Yet, where any of these deep-rooted plants grow, man can get water.

Ever since our first visit to the arid lands in the Southwest, we have been aware that the coolest place to have lunch in the open is under the shade of a clump of cottonwood trees. For eyes grown weary with the dull vegetation of desert country, the bright green of their leaves is a welcome change. Until recently we did not realize how much these natural oases deprive of water the less-adapted plants around. From the soil the cottonwoods and mesquites draw a truly phenomenal amount of moisture, and then release most of it into dry air. In man-made wells close to clumps of these two trees in the Escalente Desert of Utah, Walter N. White noticed a conspicuous lowering of the water that began between 9 and 11 each morning, and reached its lowest point between 6 and 7 P.M. As soon as the sun set, the cottonwoods and mesquites ceased to use and release so much water; new supplies percolated from underground streams, slowly raising the level in the wells again. When the trees were dormant in winter, or removed altogether, the water level in the wells remained unchanged all day.

Ranchers in Texas calculate that one inch of rainfall on an acre can produce either 166 pounds of mesquite or 500 pounds of grass. The mesquite can be used only as firewood, whereas the grass would feed three sheep for almost a month. Some men prove this claim by hard work: they replace the water-wasting trees with desirable native or adapted grasses. Then they keep their flocks and herds moving on a schedule that gives the grass plenty of time to recover and seed itself. Usually these people are rehabilitating land that once was prairie—prairie so rich that our forefathers fought the Mexicans to keep it. In the intervening years, excessive grazing destroyed the native grasses and let the inedible trees take over.

While visiting our country, the eminent soil conservationist Dr. Yaaqov Orev was impressed by the similarity he saw between some arid parts of Texas and the land familiar to him around Tel Aviv, Israel. In both, the activities of man had changed a once-fertile area into one that seemed worthless because of chronic drought. Here in Texas could be traced the change recorded in the chapters of Genesis, and then a way to reverse it that offered hope for the Near East and other semiarid lands.

Dr. Orev thought of the patriarch Abraham as a successful rancher in about 1500 B.C., taking his flocks and his family from the irrigated valley lands of the Euphrates and Tigris, going westward in search of greener pastures. Among the rolling hills of Canaan, to the east of the Mediterranean, Abraham found what he sought: abundant grass, in a land not yet overpopulated. He settled, but soon experienced a drought (Chapter 12) and then conflict over grazing rights (Chapter 13).

Right in the middle of the story about the planned sacrifice of Isaac (Chapter 22), Dr. Orev sees a parallel to the transformation of the Texas prairies into a thorn forest in a single human generation. Abraham must have known the adjacent mountain as a grass-clad slope, for he "took the wood of the burnt offering, and laid it upon Isaac his son" as they went up the trail. But, before the story ends, the mountain has a cover of thorn scrub suitable for firewood. It is so dense that the distressed father can discover "behind him a ram caught in a thicket by his horns."

Within about three hundred years, the thorny trees took over so completely that stock raising ceased in Canaan. Unable to make a living from a land in which water seemed to have vanished, Jacob and his tribe moved to Egypt. There food could still be grown because of the annual flooding of the Nile. For nearly four centuries the Jews remained in slavery, always dreaming of a return to the "good old days," to a Canaan that would be "overflowing with milk and honey." When finally their descendants did travel to their ancestral home, they found it a tangle of scrub oaks and pistacias supporting as many people as there was water for. The brush concealed wild beasts, such as the lion Samson met (Judges 14), and grew thick enough to hide David during his days as an outlaw (I Samuel 20). A mounted man, riding carelessly through it, could catch his long hair on low branches, as Absalom is recorded as doing (II Samuel 18).

Now Dr. Orev hopes for an end to the water-wasting thorn scrub that is still the conspicuous vegetation in a land whose grassy plains once satisfied Abraham the stockman so completely. In Israel, as in modern Texas, the future brightens when the soil and its water are restored to a stage of harmonious balance.

It matters little whether the land and the living

things that grow there lose the water they need because it evaporates quickly or because it passes them by on its way to the sea. Both losses to land life fit the old adage "Haste maketh waste," which John Heywood in 1546 wrote into his book of English *Proverbes*. The earth needs time to use the water that falls, as though it were savoring this gift from the skies.

We know our own place in the cycle of water. We see that the sun yields the power for the planet. So long as its energy comes beaming our way, so long will the mountain slopes catch moisture from the winds. Down myriad channels the water will swirl. Yet, if man's hand is harsh, the springs of life go dry. To induce the earth to yield generously with all that we need, we have only to show respect and understanding for the natural processes that link us firmly to the world we share with other living things.

With human populations sharing together, we have more than 150,000 new reasons each day—new lives added beyond the number who die—to use every known means to conserve our resources. Together all nations have reached the time of test, the point at which earlier cultures in their isolation faltered and crumbled. We know their history and can read the mystic writing on the wall. It is our turn to choose, to use the sweet water wisely or to see our way of life follow the others, like water over the dam.

EPILOGUE

As we contemplate what we know about fresh water, we feel calm in the eye of a storm. Round us whirl the winds of controversy, with facts lifting ideas before our eyes like straws. Some of the straws must point the direction that the storm will take. It is the one in which we all should move before the facts press too vigorously upon us. But which ideas should become our guides, and which merely distract from the action that will count?

If what we know is put to use, we see no cause to fear the future. For, although the world's fresh water has been wasted recklessly, still it returns from the sky as pure as ever. The same sun that dries the dew in the desert is constantly recharging the air above the oceans toward a new supply of rain and dew upon the land. From the past and present we can learn to nudge the future in directions that suit us better. Only thrift seems unavoidable, if so many are to use a limited resource.

The supply of water cannot be stretched, but it can be husbanded if we stretch ourselves to match our imagined needs. Surely this is the way that each of us can affirm, along with Britain's former poet laureate Robert Bridges:

> I live on hope and that I think do all
> Who come into this world.

GRACE NOTES

So many lines of interest radiate from each body of water that we have been able to touch on only a sampling—those that seem to us most hopeful and pertinent in the setting of the present. Many of the details provide fascinating reading. Some of the facts seem pregnant with promise. With this in mind, we mention here a *few* books, articles and facts from which we have gained particular delight or which we found essential to our own understanding.

CHAPTER 1: OUR PORTABLE OCEAN
p. 15   United States Department of Agriculture, *Water: Yearbook of Agriculture, 1955.* (Washington, D.C., Superintendent of Documents), xiii + 751 pp.

CHAPTER 2: WATER WAYS
p. 25   Thomas, W. L., Jr., edit., *Man's Role in Changing the Face of the Earth* (Chicago, University of Chicago Press, 1956), 1193 pp.
p. 27   Actually, a pint of water weighs 1.04 pounds.

CHAPTER 3: TILL THE WELL RUNS DRY
p. 38   Leopold, Luna B., "Rivers" in *American Scientist*, vol. 50, no. 4, pp. 511-537 (1962).
p. 38   1 square mile = 640 acres
         1 acre-foot of water = 43,560 cubic feet = 325,872 gallons
         1 ton of water = 240 gallons.

CHAPTER 4: DILUTION IS NO SOLUTION
p. 59   At the 1963 meeting, UNESCO joined with the World Meteorological Organization and the International Union of Geodesy and Geophysics in plans for an International Decade for Scientific Hydrology to be launched on January 1, 1965. From the data collected, the experts hoped to be able to draw up water budgets for entire continents, toward making the fullest practicable use of fresh waters.
p. 72   United States Department of Health, Education, and Wel-

fare, *Pollution-caused Fish Kills in 1961* (Washington, D.C., Superintendent of Documents), 21 pp.

CHAPTER 5: DEAD WATER

p. 76   United States Department of Agriculture, *Land and Water Resources: A Policy Guide* (Washington, D.C., Superintendent of Documents; 1962), 73 pp.

p. 77   Alderdice, D. F., and M. E. Worthington, "Toxicity of a DDT forest spray to young salmon," in *Canadian Fish Culturist*, issue 24, pp. 41-48 (1959).

p. 77   Ide, Fred P., "Effect of forest spraying with DDT on aquatic insects of salmon streams," in *Transactions of the American Fisheries Society*, vol. 86, pp. 108-119 (1957).

p. 77   Keenleyside, M. H. A., "Effects of spruce budworm control on salmon and other fishes in New Brunswick," in *Canadian Fish Culturist*, issue 24, pp. 17-22 (1959).

p. 79   See item for p. 72.

p. 80   The standards set for drinking water for human consumption are too lenient also for irrigation water. The maximum for agricultural use is 700, not 1,000 parts per million, with special restrictions on sodium (not over 75, and better below 61) and boron (not over 2.0, and better below 0.5).

p. 81   Milne, Lorus J., and Margery Milne, *The Balance of Nature* (New York, Alfred A. Knopf), ix + 329 + vii pp.

p. 84   United States Department of Health, Education, and Welfare, *The Struggle for Clean Water* (Washington, D.C., Superintendent of Documents; 1962), 21 pp.

p. 84   See item for p. 72.

CHAPTER 6: THE NEW RAIN GODS

p. 92   Soberman, Robert K., "Noctilucent clouds," in *Scientific American*, vol. 208, no. 6, pp. 50-59 (June, 1963).

p. 99   Schaefer, Vincent J., "The production of ice crystals in a cloud of supercooled water droplets," in *Science*, vol. 104, no. 2707, pp. 457-459 (1946).

p. 100   The seeding of clouds with particles of solid carbon dioxide was actually tried, with limited success, from an airplane in 1930 by August V. Veraart of the Netherlands. Three years later, the Swedish meteorologist Tor Bergeron satisfied himself that many raindrops reaching earth began as ice crystals, which melted on their way down.

p. 100   In 1963, the Japanese chemist Norihiko Fukuta of Negoya University reported in *Nature* that the simple and inexpensive organic compound metaldehyde was even more efficient in inducing artificial rain when seeded into clouds.

p. 100   Vonnegut, Bernard, "Experiments with silver iodide smokes in the natural atmosphere," in *Bulletin of the American Meteorological Society*, vol. 31, no. 5, pp. 151-157 (1950).

p. 101   Krick, Irving P., "Increasing water resources through weather modification," in *Journal of the American Water Works Association*, vol. 44, pp. 996-1020 (1052).

CHAPTER 7: EACH MISTY, MOISTY MORNING

p. 109   Von Humboldt, Alexander, and A. Bonpland, *Personal Narrative of Travels to the Equinoctial Regions of America*. Translated and edited by Thomasina Ross (London, Henry G. Bohn, 1852), 3 vols.

p. 110   A very different explanation is offered by E. A. Menninger, "Tropical Rain Trees," in *Journal of the New York Botanic Garden*, vol. 47, pp. 296–299 (1946). He cites various observers in support of the conclusion that "Most of the showers from tropical rain trees are caused by insects—hemipterous species, aphids, cicadas, or frog hoppers. . . ."

p. 111   White, Gilbert, *The Natural History and Antiquities of Selborne, in the County of Southampton* (London, Benjamin White & Son, 1788).

p. 113   See item for p. 25

CHAPTER 8: GREEN UMBRELLAS TO HOLD THE WATER

p. 123   Johnson, E. A., and J. L. Kovner, "Effect on streamflow of cutting a forest understory," in *Forest Science*, vol. 2, pp. 82-91 (1956).

p. 124   United States Department of Agriculture, *Soil Yearbook of Agriculture, 1957* (Washington, D.C., Superintendent of Documents), xiii + 784 pp.

p. 124   Gaiser, R. N., "Root channels and roots in forest soils," in *Proceedings of the Soil Science Society of America*, vol. 16, pp. 62-65 (1952).

CHAPTER 9: WETLANDS

p. 133   See item for p. 76.

Shaw, Samuel P., and C. Gordon Fredine, "Wetlands of the United States: Their Extent and Their Value to Waterfowl and Other Wildlife," *Circular 39*, United States Department of the Interior, Fish and Wildlife Service (1956).

CHAPTER 10: SEA FLAVOR

p. 150   Bloch, M. R., "The social influence of salt," in *Scientific American*, volume 209, no. 1, pp. 89-98 (July, 1963).

p. 151   Sverdrup, H. U., M. W. Johnson, and R. H. Fleming. *The Oceans: Their Physics, Chemistry, and General Biology* (New York: Prentice-Hall, 1942), x + 1087 pp.

p. 156   Dahl, L. K., M. Heine and L. Tassinari, "High salt content of Western infant's diet: possible relationship to hypertension in the adult," in *Nature*, vol. 198, no. 4886, pp. 1204-1205 (1963).

p.   158   Schmidt-Nielsen, Knut, and Bodil Schmidt-Nielsen, "Water metabolism of desert mammals" in *Physiological Reviews*, vol. 32, no. 2, pp. 135-166 (1952).

CHAPTER 11: GOING LONGER WITHOUT WATER
p. 166   Schmidt-Nielsen, Knut, Bodil Schmidt-Nielsen, S. A. Jarnum, and T. R. Haupt, *Body Temperature of the Camel and Its Relation to Water Economy* (Durham, N.C., Duke University Press, 1959); also Schmidt-Nielsen, Knut, "The physiology of the camel," in *Scientific American*, vol. 201, no. 1, pp. 140-151 (Dec. 1959).

CHAPTER 12: LOOK TO THE SEA
p. 186   Fänge, R., K. Schmidt-Nielsen, and H. Osaki, "The salt gland of the herring gull," in *Biological Bulletin*, vol. 115, no. 2, pp. 162-171 (1958).

p. 189 $1.00 per 1,000 gallons = $7.48 per 100 cubic feet = $325.90 per acre-foot.

p. 190   Dodge, Barnett F., "Fresh water from saline waters," in *American Scientist*, vol. 48, no. 4, pp. 476-513 (1960).

p. 191   Snyder, Asa E., "Desalting water by freezing," in *Scientific American*, vol. 207, no. 6, pp. 41-47 (December, 1962).

p. 193   Revelle, Roger, "Water," in *Scientific American*, vol. 209, no. 3, pp. 92-108 (September, 1963).

p. 193   Nace, R. L., "Water of the world," in *Natural History*, vol. 73, no. 1, pp. 10-19 (January, 1964).

p. 196   Deevey, E. S. Jr., "The human population," in *Scientific American*, vol. 203, no. 3, pp. 195-204 (September, 1960).

CHAPTER 13: NEW WAYS FOR OLD
p. 207   See item for p. 15.

p. 214   Isaac, Erich, "On the domestication of cattle," in *Science*, vol. 137, no. 3525, pp. 195-204 (1962).
See item for p. 25.

p. 219   Dasmann, R. F., and A. Mossman, "The economic value of Rhodesian game," in *Rhodesian Farmer*, vol. 30, no. 51, pp. 17-20; also "Commercial utilization of game animals on a Rhodesian ranch," in *Wild Life* (Nairobi) vol. 3, no. 3, pp. 7-14 (1961).

p. 219   Darling, F. Fraser, "Wild life husbandry in Africa," in *Scientific American*, vol. 203, no. 5, pp. 123-134 (1961).

CHAPTER 14: THE GENIUS OF WATER

p. 229   The Merchants Association of New York, *The Water Supply of the City of New York* (New York: Isaac H. Blanchard Co., 1900), 670 pp. Contains a report by Croes on "The history, condition and needs of the New York City water supply and restriction of waste of water," and by Crowell on "The use and waste of water in New York City."

p. 230   Hirshleifer, Jack, James C. de Haven, and J. W. Milliman, *Water Supply: Economics, Technology, and Policy* (Chicago, University of Chicago Press, 1960), ix + 378 pp.

p. 234   Shantz, H. L., "History and problems of arid lands development," in *The Future of Arid Lands*, edited by Gilbert F. White (Washington, D.C., American Association for the Advancement of Science, 1956) pp. 3-25.

CHAPTER 15: WATER OVER THE DAM

p.240   White, Gilbert F., *The Changing Role of Water in Arid Lands* (Tucson, University of Arizona Press, 1960), 15 pp.

p. 251   Hockensmith, Roy D., edit., *Water and Agriculture* (Washington, D.C., American Association for the Advancement of Science, 1960), 198 pp.

p. 253   See item for p. 15, also item for p. 251.

p. 254   Orev, Yaaqov, "Brush invasion—1500 B.C. and 1950 A.D.," in *Journal of Range Management*, vol. 9, no. 1, pp. 6-7 (1956).

INDEX